Dr. Borlaug is already established as the prime candidate for the title of human being who has brought most benefit to humanity during his lifetime.
John White, CBE, Pro Chancellor, De Montfort University, England

[Borlaug's seeds] gave us respect in our own eyes. India was no longer a nation going around with a begging bowl ... We could feed ourselves.
T.N. Khoshoo, Government of India Department of Environment

By his scientific skill, robust faith, and an all-consuming sense of urgency, Dr. Borlaug has rendered to India-Pakistan a service which is unique and unforgettable.
Sudhir Sen, **A Richer Harvest**

While environmental activists sought to instill fear of the food supply, Norman Borlaug used common sense and courage to eliminate famine in countries where it had been the historic norm.
Malcolm Wallop, Former United States Senator

Norman Borlaug is the world's most important environmental statesman. By squeezing more production from the farmland, he and those who followed him kept agriculture within bounds while a soaring population demanded that food production quadruple. These few pioneers spared more land for nature than anyone before or since.
E.C.A. Runge, Texas A&M University

The power of Norm's legacy is rooted in his ability to deliver his message to peasants and presidents with equal dignity and candor. For forty years he has been helping people feed themselves. He caused things to happen.
Dale Harpstead, Michigan State University

"The man we need now is Norman Borlaug."
President Josiah Bartlett, January, 17, 2001
[facing an intractable famine in The West Wing, a popular TV show]

Throughout [the Borlaug] story runs a hopeful and transcendent theme—the triumph of peaceful efforts at human betterment over the destructive effect of war.
Donald Paarlberg, U. S. Department of Agriculture

Norm is the only practicing plant breeder to win the Nobel Prize, and the only scientist to win the Peace Prize for his work in science.
Robert W. Herdt, The Rockefeller Foundation

He is neither intimidating nor intimidated, being as comfortable with kings and presidents and government leaders as he is squatting in front of a mud hut conversing with a peasant farmer.
George Cummins, Iowa State University

Borlaug's unique combination of technical innovation, idealism, energy and impatience with bureaucratic inefficiency took entire countries from starvation to self-sufficiency within a few years.
Biographical Essay – World of Genetics

BOOKS BY NOEL VIETMEYER

For Bracing Books

Borlaug: Right off the Farm. 1914 – 1944*
Borlaug: Wheat Whisperer. 1944 – 1959*
Borlaug: Bread Winner. 1960 – 1969*
Norman Borlaug's Heroes [in preparation]

For National Academy of Sciences

NEW CROPS

Lost Crops of Africa: Volume 1 – Grains*
Lost Crops of Africa: Volume 2 – Vegetables
Lost Crops of Africa: Volume 3 - Fruits
Lost Crops of the Incas
Underexploited Tropical Plants
Tropical Legumes
The Winged Bean: A High-Protein Crop for the Humid Tropics
Amaranth: Modern Prospects for an Ancient Crop*
Jojoba: A New Crop for Arid Lands*
Quality-Protein Maize*
Triticale: A Promising Addition to the World's Cereal Grains*
Vetiver: A Thin Green Line Against Erosion*
Guayule: An Alternative Source of Natural Rubber
Neem: A Tree for Solving Global Problems
Leucaena: Promising Forage and Tree Crop for the Tropics
Mangium and Other Fast-Growing Acacias*
Calliandra: A Versatile Tree for the Humid Tropics*
Casuarinas: Nitrogen-Fixing Trees for Adverse Sites*
Firewood Crops: Shrub and Tree Species for Energy*

NEW ANIMAL RESOURCES

Water Buffalo: New Prospects for an Underutilized Animal*
Butterfly Farming *
Crocodiles as a Resource for the Tropics*
Little-Known Asian Animals with Promising Economic Futures*
Microlivestock*

NEW IDEAS

Ferrocement: Applications in Developing Countries
Making Aquatic Weeds Useful
Mosquito Control: Perspectives for Developing Countries
More Water for Arid Lands*
Sowing Forests from the Air*
Producer Gas: Another Fuel for Motor Transport*

* Available (while supplies last) from **BracingBooks.com**, see p310

BORLAUG

VOLUME 3

Bread Winner, 1960 - 1969

NOEL VIETMEYER

BRACING BOOKS
LORTON, VIRGINIA

BORLAUG; Volume 3, Bread Winner. 1960 - 1969. Copyright © 2004, 2010 by Noel Vietmeyer

Version 1.0: October 2010.

Library of Congress Cataloguing-in-Publication Data

Vietmeyer, Noel Duncan, 1940-

ISBN 978-0-578-06920-3

Biography & Autobiography/Science & Technology

BRACING BOOKS
5921 River Drive
Lorton, VA 22079-4128
USA

Printed in the United States of America

Signature Book Printing, www.sbpbooks.com

CONTENTS

ILLUSTRATIONS x

PRONUNCIATION GUIDE xii

PROLOGUE 1

INTRODUCTION 7

Chapter 1   1960   Pain 19

Chapter 2   1961   Apostles 35

Chapter 3   1962   Perspectives 53

Chapter 4   1963   Pivot 67

Chapter 5   1964   Plants 89

Chapter 6   1965   Prospects 111

Chapter 7   1966   Perils 129

Chapter 8   1967   Proofs 159

Chapter9   1968   Production 181

Chapter 10   1969   Perfection 199

AFTERWORD by Norman Borlaug 223

AUTHOR'S NOTE 227

CAREER SAVERS 234

ACKNOWLEDGEMENTS 236

PICTURE CREDITS 238

ILLUSTRATIONS

Mexico (map) 18

Friends (Borlaug and Wheat) 20

Career Saver #27 (Al Moseman) 23

Seeds that Started Stampedes 28-9

Wheat Apostles I, 1961 38-9

Career Saver #28 (Reyes Vega) 41

Wheat Wealth 42

Home Life 44

Coach and Class 46-7

International Rice Research Institute 50

Wheat Apostles II, 1962 56-7

Career Saver #29 (Eva Villegas) 59

South Asia (map) 62-3

Career Saver #30 (Ralph Cummings) 70

Rural India . . . Before Borlaug 72-3

Career Saver #31 (M.S. Swaminathan) 75

Career Saver #32 (Haldore Hanson) 80

Career Saver #33 (Adolfo López Mateos) 85

Career Saver #34 (Malik Khuda Bakhsh) 92

Career Saver #35 (Chidambara Subramaniam) 96

Wheat Apostles IV, 1964 100-1

Career Saver #36 (Glenn Anderson) 105

Career Saver #37 (Ayub Khan) 113

Career Saver #38 (George Killion) 116

Orville Freeman 125

Career Saver #39 (Ignacio Narvaez) 132

The Old Guard (VKVR Rao) 137

Seed Shipment (trucks and sacks) 144

Seed Shipment (ship loading) 145

Career Saver #40 (Staley Pitts) 150

Career Saver #41 (Yaqui Vargas) 152-3

ILLUSTRATIONS (cont.)

Smiles Hiding Horrors 156

Change Comes Quietly 162-3

Guarding the Seed 175

After Borlaug 184-5

Signal Honor 189

The Leader Honors Science 192-3

Tour of Triumph 196-7

Wheat Apostles 202-3

Rural India . . . After Borlaug 206-7

Honoring the Savior 208

Torch Gets Passed 209

The Dupe (Yahya Khan) 211

Norman Borlaug and the author 244

PRONUNCIATION GUIDE

PEOPLE
Borlaug	BOR-LOG
Calles [Rodolfo]	KY-es
Eva [Villegas]	EH-vah
Harrar	ha-RAH
Maurer	MAO-rer
Narvaez	nar-VY-es
Obregón	oh-breg-ON
Stakman	STAKE-man
Sivaraman	seeva-RAH-man
Swaminathan	swah-mee-NAH-than
Subramaniam	soobra-MAN-ee-am
Villegas [Eva]	vee-AY-gas
Ayub Khan	EYE-oob karn
Yahya Khan	YAH-YAH karn

PLACES
Bihar	bee-HAR
Ciudad (city)	see-oo-DAHD
Hermosillo	ermo-SEE-oh
Punjab	puhn-JARB
Toluca	tol-OO-kah
Uttar Pradesh	oo-tah prah-DESH
Valle [valley]	VY-YEH
Yaqui	YAH-kee

PLANTS
Cajeme	cah-HEM-ee
Lerma Rojo	LEHR-mah ROH-hoh
Kentana	ken-TAH-na
Pitic	PIT-EEK
Penjamo	pen-HAR-moe
Siete Cerros	see-ET-ee SAIR-os

ORGANIZATIONS
CIANO	see-AH-no
CIMMYT	SIM-it
Ejidal	eh-HEE-dal
Patronato	pat-ron-AH-toh
PRONASE	pro-NAH-see

Norman Borlaug died September 12, 2009

By then, the manuscript for this book was in advanced preparation and he had already reviewed, commented on and approved the basic text.

In particular he had seen and approved my general rendering of the quotes, which are mostly taken from our conversations during 25 years.

I've also substituted American measures—pounds per acre, for example—even when quoting Norm, who more commonly used metric units.

Noel Vietmeyer

PROLOGUE

FOR MOST OF OUR million-year journey there was no food supply. Humans ate when Nature allowed. Life was a silent struggle with outraged stomachs interspersed by happy flings with fullness when plants and animals chose to dispense something edible.

Nature being so heartless, haunting and homicidal the species could barely sustain itself. Anyone surviving 30 years was more than blessed – they were aged. Human numbers consequently failed to reach 1 billion *until 1814*.

Soon thereafter we learned to store and ship food, and could finally stuff our stomachs between harvests. Year-round eating transformed the human condition: food fell from master to servant, seasonal starvation retreated into remission, and babies began blossoming, the aged began aging, and the species began multiplying.

Within a mere century that multiplication was getting out of hand:

- By Norman Borlaug's birth (1914) we had hit *1.6 billion;*
- By his 20th birthday (1934) we'd reached *2 billion;*
- By his 50th birthday (1964) we were *3 billion*, with that many more scheduled to come before the 20th century ended.

This book features that decade of the 1960s wherein Borlaug and the 20th century confront midlife crises. Food production is maxed out, humans are at carrying capacity, 3 billion more are headed earthward, and most will find the pantry bare.

The horror of looming global famine jolted world leaders such as the jaunty young war hero still unpacking his bags in the White House. For his presidency John F. Kennedy declared two goals: landing a man on the moon *and fighting famine*. "The war against hunger," he told the world, "is truly Mankind's war of liberation."

JFK's vision reflected the belief that humanity's favored faction should share its good fortune. The mantra of the moment was: "There is NO hunger problem – just a distribution problem."

But even as the new president spoke, his country was flooding the hungry continents with grain and Nature was once again preparing to cap human numbers.

America's ascension to world food bank resulted from the rural revolution that had buttressed Norm Borlaug during his teenage years. Our man of destiny had experienced the wondrous uplift that hybrid corn, fertilizer, tractors, electricity and all-weather roads brought to farm country during the 1920s and '30s.

Sadly, the Great Depression and World War II hid that magnificent makeover from outside gaze. But in the 1950s American farmers began disgorging a surplus so huge it could be shared with the world.

Now mostly forgotten, this global generosity far surpassed the famous Marshall Plan that had fed and fortified war-ravaged Europeans a decade earlier. The new and expanded version for feeding Asians, Africans and Latin Americans was the brainchild of a World War II tank commander who'd helped run that European rescue.

Following a trip to India, Gwynn Garnett grasped how the happy half could feed the hungry half.

First he spotted the fundamental problem:

- The under-fed masses live far, far away;
- Food is bulky, perishable, very expensive to handle; and
- The hungry lack the cash to buy anything.

Then he spotted the solution:

- Let the hungry lands pay *in their own currencies*;
- Reinvest those monies for good works in their own societies; and
- Donate part of the food to the truly destitute.

Garnett said this generosity would pay for itself by spawning goodwill and opening great markets for American goods.

Agreeing with this logic was Hubert Humphrey. As Borlaug's classmate at the University of Minnesota, Humphrey had been too poor to buy a textbook, but by 1950 he'd managed to make something of himself. As a leader in the U.S. Congress he helped turn Garnett's vision into Public Law 480.

Soon thereafter hundreds of American freighters were toting wheat across the seas to the hungry continents far, far away. Rebranded "Food for Peace" in 1961, this fabulous food-sharing made Americans proud. We were feeding the postwar world, fostering friendship, furthering the causes of peace and prosperity, and recycling rupees and other colorful currencies into good works that would elevate the world's benighted masses into clamoring customers.

India was Food for Peace's largest client. There, in the most perilous country of the most populous continent, people production outstripped food production by 5 percent a year. As this book's decade opens, many of the 400 million Indians would be struggling with outraged stomachs had not America been dispensing edibles for almost a decade.

But by 1960 India's case of congenital hunger seems incurable. More than half the vast land area is under cultivation and most of that is overused. There are no more forests to cut, swamps to drain or deserts to water. Crops can barely carry their current loads. Food reserves are nonexistent. The treasury is bare, ruling out purchases on the open market. And every month brings a million more mouths.

Only Hubert Humphrey's freighter flotilla stretching back around the globe keeps the comatose Subcontinent from succumbing. Some years that flotilla carries a fifth of America's amber waves of grain *just to India*.

This massive rescue might have been good had an endgame been in sight or had Garnett's predictions been panning out. Sadly, though, India showed little gratitude and rejected outright friendship. Peace was not prospering: India was actually in an arms race with its neighbor Pakistan. Prosperity was not prospering, either: India's masses remained impoverished. Foreign goods were indeed being bought, but the big-ticket purchases were armaments and nuclear devices from the Soviet Union. As to recycling its rupees, the United States had earned so many it couldn't spend half its horde without cracking India's eggshell economy.

Furthermore, just as the jaunty fresh-faced president unpacked his last bag and tried to rally the world, Hunger was claiming hegemony over scores of nations beyond India.

That is how things stand as we rejoin the Borlaug saga.

A whole generation is on trial.

Hunger is going global and going guerilla.

Handing out free food willy-nilly is proving a failure.

The situation is hopeless; the authorities helpless.

There's not enough food to accommodate the current 3 billion.

No one knows what to do to stave off catastrophe as 3 billion more try to join the unhappy human race.

BORLAUG

VOLUME 3

Bread Winner, 1960 - 1969

1914 - 1959

INTRODUCTION

THE THIRD IN A SERIES exploring fate and the fortunes of Norman Borlaug, this book follows on from *Wheat Whisperer 1944-1959*, which featured the neverending dramas attending Borlaug's first 15 years in Mexico.

Back in 1944 when he'd arrived, Mexico had worn the haunted look of hunger; malnourishment and bony babies were common sights. One of four young agriculturists the Rockefeller Foundation sent to forestall famine, Borlaug had been hired largely because of a professor's casual assertion: "He has great depth of courage and determination. He will not be defeated by difficulty and he burns with a missionary zeal."

After competently commanding a bulldozer and fashioning fields for research on corn and beans the 30 year old plant pathologist had been assigned the mind-bending task of fixing the wheat crop. Ranking among the world's worst, Mexico produced only 300,000 tons a year and farmers were quitting in despair or disgust.

Nobody could be expected to stop, let alone reverse, wheat's decline. But during the next decade and a half – despite relentless opposition from time, nature, misguided bosses, misinformed public, prissy pundits, snooty peers and suspicious farmers – he produced a string of high-yielding, fast-maturing, disease-resisting varieties that more than doubled each acre's output. Along the way thousands of growers re-embraced their old crop with gusto, even glee, and Mexico's annual output soared fourteen-fold to surpass 5 million tons.

Had this magnificent makeover come from an organized group and a career-long campaign, history would have honored it. However this was the work of a solitary scientist and a few helpers, many of them barely literate village kids. They relied on makeshift facilities, lived in miserable quarters, operated under demanding conditions, received minimal wages and only modest financial support. They fed a hungry nation on the cheap and on the hop. And history paid no heed.

The secret behind the success was a pair of sites whose contrary climates permitted continuous cropping. Each year saw a winter sowing in the northern desert state of Sonora followed by a summer sowing on a mountainside near the city of Toluca. Wheat being a 5-month crop, squeezing in two plantings a year a thousand miles apart left no time for rest or relaxation but it compressed 30 years of progress into 15.

As an unexpected bonus, cycling the best plant lines through sequential stints in the contrasting climates evolved varieties that could master diverse latitudes, seasons, soils and disease threats. These were plants with legs. Although no one then knew it, they could populate the world's wheatlands without the customary decade of fine-tuning.

Now as we take up the story for the third time, Borlaug has spent a third of his 45 years freeing Mexico from hunger's haunting shadow. Sonora's Yaqui Valley, formerly the world's worst wheatland, now ranks among the great granaries. The sleepy, dusty, frontier settlement he'd stumbled into in 1944 has by 1959 morphed into Mexico's most modern and most prosperous metropolis. Obregón City's skyline is dominated by big breweries, big bakeries and big-sky silos serving companies cashing in on the abundance of grain. Borlaug-built wheat is being brewed into world famous beers; baked into billions of tortillas, breads and cookies; and boxed into popular breakfast cereals. Mexican food itself is undergoing a makeover as the plentiful, cheap, mass-manufactured flour tortilla soars in popularity. Mexican diets are improving; mass malnourishment and bony babies are no longer seen.

Though initially resentful of the gringo too dumb to speak Spanish, the local wheat farmers have become friends and fans. One tells a camera crew that "The best thing that happened to the Yaqui Valley was the coming of Dr. Borlaug."

They've made their gratitude plain. Among other things, they've rescued him from deportation by their own government and saved his program from destruction by his own superiors in New York. They've built him the world's best wheat-research station. And they *voluntarily* tax their own earnings to support its operations.

Any normal human would hereby retire and relegate the remainder of his days to collecting accolades.

But, as you'll see, this is no normal human.

That book featuring the dramas attending his Mexican triumph followed on from *Right off the Farm 1914-1944*, which featured the dramas attending the preceding 30 years while he remained in his native land. That opening volume of the series showed how Norman Borlaug's motivation got molded, his special strengths got sculpted, and his attitudes got properly adjusted before fortune plucked him from obscurity and pushed him over the southern border to banish hunger's haunting shadow from the failing state next door.

Those personal qualities were fashioned during his formative years before he left his homeland were surprising. They included:

Empathy with peasants. Despite his PhD, Borlaug never forgot that he was himself a log-cabin product, born on a small impoverished farm in Iowa's northeastern corner. His family labored solely to eat and solely by hand. They were what economists call "subsistence farmers" but society called "peasants."

Farmers in 1914 relied on the agronomy of the ancients. Less a profession than a prison, this lowest and hardest means for staving off starvation allowed for no alternative life. Horizons were so closed that the Borlaugs and their neighbors normally conversed in the Norwegian of their ancestors and felt closer to clan than country. The world beyond the village was an alien universe where people talked funny.

On that tiny farm near Cresco drudgery was the currency of every day. Absent machinery, animals plowed the fields and powered the operations. Absent electricity, appliances could not lessen the burden let alone light the night. Absent asphalt, the Borlaugs were marooned whenever rain or snowmelt morphed Howard County's dirt trails into mud traps. Absent fertilizer and strong seeds, the under-performing corn, oats, pasture and hay pinned the family on poverty's edge.

To the Borlaugs eating was everything. Absent a social support system, there were no food stamps or anything else to fall back on. They had to produce their own edibles, and producing enough of them to tide the family through every day of every year was a supreme challenge. The likelihood of hunger during the next Iowa winter when plants would quit dispensing edibles, was everpresent. Most of the berries, cherries, apples and plums picked from their roadsides or from their few fruit trees got crammed into Mason jars. That bottled life-insurance residing on the kitchen shelf, together with a few bags of cornmeal and some potatoes and rutabagas surviving in sand barrels in the basement, had to keep starvation at bay for six months.

Then, starting in the 1920s, the subsistence life got overthrown as the Midwest underwent agriculture's first magnificent makeover. This was the miraculous moment when the ancients' hard agronomy died. Within little more than a decade, high-yield corn, tractors, all-weather roads, fertilizer, and electricity triumphed over the method by which serfs had fed Julius Caesar. Hybrid corn doubled the output and doubled the income; fertilizer and the tractor each doubled them yet again. The Borlaug's got their first spending money.

More importantly for our story, these modern marvels defeated drudgery. No longer was a lad's muscle necessary to a family's maintenance. Norm Boy Borlaug could explore prospects in the alien universe beyond the village confines. Perhaps he might become someone.

For this particular farm lad liberation from the locked-down life proved so joyous he would devote the rest of his days to helping peasants across the globe find the same glorious freedom.

Gratitude. He'd been 30 years old when he steered a ten-year-old jalopy across the Texas border and into the mysteries of Mexico. By then he was well on the way to becoming someone. His success had come courtesy of a cast of kindly characters who'd each provided him a chance to reach for a star.

Among these angels of deliverance was a grade school teacher who'd intervened to get him into high school; a wrestling coach who'd turned him into an athlete; a football star who'd almost physically forced him to attend the University of Minnesota; a fast-food company and a sorority who'd saved him from starvation while he was penniless; and a professor who enticed him into agricultural science when he much preferred forestry. Also there was Margaret Gibson, who'd shared with him the horrors of being a student pauper during the Great Depression and who in 1937 became his wife.

As he crossed the Rio Grande those absent friends are present. They'd made him whole. And he was heading south to pay forward his debt. He'll give Mexicans the chance to reach for their stars.

A memory of hunger. The primal fear of not being able to eat had been in the background of most of those three decades. Though even as a child he'd dined well by the standards of humanity's past, the fear of nature failing to dispense edibles remained branded in the brain.

So too did the remembrance of his first days in the parallel universe where people talked funny and you didn't have to grow your own food. At the University of Minnesota in 1933 he'd been too poor to buy anything. Absent campus dining halls, he waited tables at a coffee shop. The pay was pitiful: for working the breakfast rush he was allowed to take one cup of coffee, five prunes and two slices of toast. And in January 1934, when he returned to school following the Christmas break the coffee shop had closed. Hunger then became an all-day companion. He managed to scrape through on White Castle coupons, which for 10¢ provided three small hamburgers and a pint of milk, until the Alpha Omicron Pi sorority fed him in exchange for busboy duties. Then for a special wrestling meet in 1935 he'd fasted to the point of nearly losing his senses along with the last pound.

These confrontations with with the devil itself were so affecting he'd committed his life to fighting Hunger to the death.

An ability to withstand harsh conditions. As a youth Borlaug lived through appalling bouts of weather. The decade of the 1930s was the 20th Century's most climatically challenging, with the hottest summers, coldest winters, longest droughts, not to mention the Dust Bowl. During the winter of 1935 he nearly froze after someone stole his only jacket and Twin City temperatures plunged to 34 below.

Moreover he'd picked up advanced survival skills as a forestry student forced to live in the woods; cooking and camping and caring for himself. Also he'd spent the summer of 1937 in a fire lookout in the middle of the nation's largest wilderness with no protection from the only other living things: wild creatures, lightning, and the wildfires he was expected to confront – and did.

All of these were perfect preparation him for a career in Mexico's research fields. Heat, flies, mosquitoes, rats, snakes, dust, thirst were by comparison, tame. Flop house facilities were fine. Cooking over a corncob fire . . . no problem.

The soul of an athlete. Though in high school Borlaug became a star wrestler and football player, his dream of becoming somebody centered on second base at Wrigley Field. For boys of the Great Depression athletics offered almost the only way out; but farm boys like him had neither coaches nor competitions to sharpen their skills.

Borlaug was lucky that in his sophomore years his tiny high school got a new principal who happened to be perhaps the best wrestling coach in the land. David Bartlema not only brought out the boy's competitive nature he stamped it on his soul. For the rest of his days Norm repeatedly quoted Bartelma's dictum, "In the game of life you have to go into each bout with the passion to do your best." And he always likened his kind of science to an athletic contest. Opponents he faced in his own game of life included time, weather, crop disease, misguided bosses, and almost anything else you can think of.

Being so elemental, food development placed him at the storm center of society. And that explains why there's an edge about him as he spends long decades wrestling humanity's greatest opponent: Hunger. The competitive fires burning within are never far from the surface.

A feeling for wheat. When Borlaug crossed the Rio Grande he'd been hired to work on corn and beans. Only inadvertently did wheat swim into his orbit. Although he'd never encountered the plant face-to-face, he'd taken classes from E.C. Stakman, the greatest wheat specialist of that era. Young Borlaug was still a forester when he first heard the University of Minnesota professor expound on wheat's main disease, stem rust. Subsequently, he'd taken Stakman's course on plant pathology, counted stem-rust spores on Stakman's endless stream of microscope slides, and attended Stakman's seminars, many of which took place in fields of diseased wheat.

All this provided a background for a future working with the top crop. More than that, though, Stakman's all-encompassing intellect provided a vertically integrated and amazingly wide-angled vision that encompassed science, food, history and the human condition.

A strange attitude toward science. The University of Minnesota professor also inspired Borlaug's approach to research. For decades Stakman counted stem rust spores on tens of thousands of Vaseline coated microscope slides exposed to the air over Middle America. The work seemed too tedious to be science, and for most of those decades it seemed to be going nowhere. But in aggregate his data provided stunning insights. Knowing where the spores were, where they were headed, and in what concentrations at every point of the year turned the mundane measurements into a powerful portrait of a plant disease of immense complexity and destructive power. The fungus, it turned out, migrated with the seasons just like ducks. And it wintered in northern Mexico, enjoying the warmth and the wheat grown there between November and April.

Knowing all this, the 30 year old plant pathologist motoring into northern Mexico in 1944 may have had a PhD but he would use it to do things rather than discover things. This talent he'd learned while working at the DuPont Company in Delaware during the awful pressures of World War II. He'd than been under War Department orders and had to fix problems with whatever skill or science met the need.

He emerged from those experiences mentally prepared for fixing food supplies. He was an empiricist who followed facts rather than fancy theories. The panorama unspooling before his vision drew him forward as the wheat plant made the unknown known. For him, science was just the canvas; the final portrait – the product the public saw – was all that counted.

Most of his artwork was done down at the squad level; it was grunt science rather than great science. This showed particularly in his decades-long battle to build better and better wheat varieties. Each season in Mexico he sowed millions of seeds gathered from plants that were evolving the kind of qualities he sought. Then as they matured and showed their stuff he ripped out all the riff raff, hoping that by season's end at least one supremely suitable specimen will remain.

In all this he was more savvy than smart. He could take an instant impression of a wheat plant and see it complete, not just as itself but as a part of the tool kit for fixing a broken food supply.

A sense of mission. During the seemingly endless emotion and commotion stirred up while lifting Mexico's food supply he could often have succumbed to panic, pessimism or paranoia. But as each new puzzle loomed into view he merely got on with solving the most accessible and amenable pixel — focusing on the possible, preparing for setbacks and unworried about perfection. All this took immense confidence. He moved continuously and confidently from the known to the unknown, believing in himself when no one else did.

This special talent was vital. Victory several times hinged on his relentless resolve and irrepressible optimism. During his battle with stem rust, for instance, he fought that fungus like a madman for nine years, refusing to let wheat's most formidable foe beat him. And that foe really was formidable. Stem rust has molested mankind's daily bread supply since at least Biblical times. It comes in more than 300 strains, any of which can wipe out wheatlands at will. Its spores soar by the trillions through the planet's atmosphere, riding the jetstream, forever seeking a susceptible wheat plant upon which to fulfill its awful destiny and launch a new wave of terror on the food front. But after those 18 seasons of struggle Borlaug seemed to have won the match. Then the sneaky microbe mutated. He went back to the beginning and, with calm authority, duked it out for another eight rounds before stem rust finally threw in the towel.

As a result of his resolve our top food crop has remained immune to its deadly rival throughout most of our lifetimes. Thanks to him, few people nowadays have ever heard of stem rust, the gravest threat to supply of human food.

Devotion to action. Though focus and self-belief made Borlaug good, hard work made him great. Watching him operate was a sort of spectator sport. He was almost robotically efficient. People found it engrossing. Inspiring too.

Forever on his feet, he was less a living entity than a little engine endlessly trying to get over the mountain and prove it could. His natural element was the hills, the mountains, the blue sky, the green fields and the golden desert. Not for him a desk in a city or a bench in a laboratory. His command was plants; his attempts at commanding paper and office procedures proved disastrous. Though supreme at shuffling thoughts, he was shockingly inept at shuffling paper.

While working at the DuPont Company under the impress of those awful World War II duties, he'd learned the need for speed. War Department wonks would show up, toss him an impossible problem, and demand he "solve that by the end of the week!"

When you had to fix something by the end of the week perfection went out the window. He learned to focus on just finding improvement. And he carried that need for speed and partial solutions into his later career. Indeed, it was the key to his lifetime's accomplishments.

But this need for speed created a distressing inability to submit plans and paperwork and drove his bosses batty. Though he delivered results and renown, his superiors constantly pestered him for reports and receipts. But when nature is closing the curtain on the sowing season and the next research round needs launching a thousand miles away across the trackless void there's no time for writing or reviewing.

Though it created constant tension, professional precision went out the window too. He opted for progress. And the world is better for it.

Defiance of convention. Although confronting arguably the greatest technical challenge of his age, Borlaug seldom sought his peers' advice. He paid little attention to scientific papers or even newspapers; novels were total timewasters. He preferred working alone with his highly trained and dedicated apprentices. He didn't even think ahead. On leaving home before dawn each morning he had no clue when he'd return. Most times it was long after dark and dinner was cold, a detail that didn't bother him.

This separation from the rest of reality had an upside: unaware of conventional wisdom and fads of convenience, he went his own way. To others, he seemed to be following a private star. But really he was following the unfolding of insight as he progressed from the known to the unknown. That was the best read of all.

Big-tent leadership. Throughout his life this mild-mannered scientist with the sky-blue eyes, sandy hair and bright warm smile retained a boyish touch. His appearance shouted friendship without a sound. Because of this engaging aura people did more for him than they'd anticipated . . . and without being asked.

Part of this personal presence was his disarming modesty; people embraced him for his humbleness. Part of it was the fact that though he was forever striving, it was never for personal glory or gain. Part of it was an ineffable quality that made people desire to become disciples. That effect transcended rank: children gravitated; politicians and presidents put their egos in their pockets; scientists and students listened in awe. In his presence they all got self-belief and the self-confidence they could be someone.

For him, leadership and teaching were sides of the same coin. He taught almost everyone he met. He never demanded belief, let alone obedience, loyalty or commitment. He just led by example, demanding the best of himself and letting mental osmosis demand it of others.

Compassion for the young. To children he was always accessible, gracious, and concerned. Piloting young people to extraordinary attainment was as iconic a feature of his life as was his hunger fighting. During his days he helped thousands liberate themselves from locked down lives through science or sport.

In Mexico his technical support staff included a motley crew of Mexican boys, most of them scarcely literate. They began by scaring off hordes of sparrows as his fields neared maturity and accurate yield numbers were vital. Later he provided them a chance for greater things as cross-pollinators of wheat. For this, they proved as well-coordinated as cats and they made many of the gene matches that will come to feed the world. As these young societal outcasts worked at this most tedious and most testing task there was a glow in their eyes – finally someone had trusted them. Later he welcomed students from around the world into his high-powered research team and helped them become somebody. By the end, youthful enthusiasm and optimism of those acolytes will enliven politicians, scientists and farmers worldwide. Without Borlaug's "kids" the human family would not have been fed.

In sport, too, he made many nobodies into somebodies. He was always coaching, which in part is why he helped start Little League in Mexico in 1954. Some of those he coached knew nothing of his day job, but always remembered his message for living:

Give your best . . .
Believe you can succeed . . .
Face adversity squarely . . .
Be confident you'll find the answers when problems arise.
Then go out and win some bouts!

These and other personal qualities form the backdrop to all that is about to unfold. As the 1960s gets underway Borlaug is 46 and his career seems over and out.

He has no clue that the most tumultuous decade of an already too tumultuous life is about to unfold.

Nor does he realize that the inner qualities learned during his formative years and honed during his Mexican years are about to get their ultimate tests.

That self-abnegation made possible everything in our story. "My Mom provided the stability in our home," Jeanie explains. "With Daddy away so much, she did the banking and the shopping, paid the bills and managed all the family affairs. Had she not been such a strong person, either Bill or I would have been a mess or my Dad couldn't have done all he did."

Although Norm stayed in Sonora from the sowing in November through the harvest in April, he returned to the apartment for a few weeks of togetherness over Christmas and New Year. During this particular home interlude when the calendar is farewelling 1961, Jeanie is coming of age. Since September she's been attending Valparaiso University in Indiana.

Bill too has been away. Since September, he's been attending Shattuck, a high school in Faribault, Minnesota. But before leaving he'd spent the summer playing baseball for his dad. "Little League was the epicenter of our family," Bill recalls. "During the summer months there were practices on Tuesdays and Thursdays and games on Saturdays. Dad found the time to make them all."

Seven years before, Bill's allergies and health concerns had been so troublesome that Norm and his colleague John Niederhauser had introduced youth baseball to Mexico. After a shaky start it had proven a huge success and strengthened both families, not to menion Mexican families. Little League had grown into a national institution and the Monterrey team had won the Little League World Series, twice in a row.

By 1961 15,000 Mexico City boys were enjoying Little League during the summer. Bill, however, has past the age limit and graduated to Pony League, which includes kids from about 14 to 17. Games are played at the American High School baseball field. And Norm still coaches with the same vigor, joy, flair and success. That very year his team, the Toltecas, won the league and he coached them in the all star series too. Sadly, they didn't win the all stars.

Bill's Toltecas teammate Gordon (Russ) Sutton and his brother David have both recently penned their recollections. Here's Gordon's:

"In the early 1960s, I moved to Mexico City with my mother and two brothers. My father had passed away when I was twelve and my mother thought his pension would go much farther living in Mexico.

We moved to a small house in Mexico City and the first thing my Mom did was enroll us three boys in baseball.

Borlaug was both an operational leader and an inspirational one. He had the inate power to win young people's hearts and minds. "Play the game of life with passion" he often said, " . . .the passion to do your best."

. . . CLASS

Coach Borlaug issues the Toltecas a pre-game pep talk, 1961. Gordon Sutton (the one sucking on a coke) remembers: "He was hard driving, and always hollering and teaching. Nothing got past him. He really knew the fundamentals of baseball and loved to teach them. Nobody was spared criticism. His Spanish was fluent and he hollered at the Mexican players as much as us. He was extremely competitive. He didn't care who we were playing, he believed we could win. He was first on the field and last one off. He'd pitch batting practice and stand on the mound and throw balls to the players' weaknesses until they could hit the pitches. He was slight of build but extremely strong. He had muscular arms and could throw all the pitches. He also hit infield practice. He'd hit balls hard and away, making us exert ourselves to the limit. He'd constantly yell that we could do better (which we did). He expected everybody to hustle all the time and wouldn't let players dog it. But at the end of the practice we all knew his driving efforts had made us a little bit better. I'm sure he used this same inner competitive tenacity and drive when he preached agriculture.

"Margaret Borlaug was also an avid baseball fan. She came to every game to cheer us on. She was extremely vocal, and loved to holler at the umpires, who were not used to females screaming at them. She kept the crowd in stitches. What a character!"

"I was lucky enough to end up on the Toltecas. Norman Borlaug was our coach and he coached us all the way to a league championship. "What I remember most about Coach Borlaug was that he was a kind and giving man with a great work ethic. My mother did not have a car or much money and for years Coach Borlaug would pick me up every day and take me to baseball practice. At the end of practice or a game, he would drop me off at home. During the ride, win or lose, he would give me advice about baseball and his philosophy of life in general. I cherished those rides and all the wisdom he had to offer.

"When I couldn't afford a baseball glove, he gave me one. It was used, but it had a great pocket and I am sure, at one time, it belonged to his son, Bill. Once in a while, he bought my brothers and me cokes and hot dogs. Because we were poor, I am sure he helped my mom out with any fees that had to be paid for the privilege of playing baseball.

"While driving to practice, I always noticed in the far back area of his Chevy station wagon were bags and bags of small, green plants. Little did I know that I was riding with the man who was in the process of feeding the world."

Although Margaret's life since coming to Mexico had been hard, she had at least had the children for company. Now with them away at school she spent months alone. The new emptiness was troubling. She toured historic sites around Mexico City and squandered many days racing through book after book on every conceivable subject. "I got so compulsive," she later joked, "that I even started reading the small print on the cereal boxes at breakfast."

At least one thing had improved: Norm's salary. The Rockefeller Foundation now pays him like a professor in a university. While far from wealth, it was also far from worry. There's even enough dollars for Margaret to occasionally visit her brothers and father in Oklahoma and Texas, and Norm's parents and sisters in Iowa.

She longs to see the world, but has never had a chance. The two have been married since 1937 and never had a honeymoon. Norm solemnly promised he'll rectify that . . . just as soon as he can fit it in.

In 1961, after spending nearly a decade as Rockefeller Foundation president, Dean Rusk ascended to the Washington stratosphere to become Secretary of State and a Kennedy cabinet member.

Filling Rusk's foundation spot was none other than Norm's

benefactor and boss, George Harrar. Elevation to foundation president was made on the basis of the accomplishments in Mexico. And it was deserved. Toward his understudy Harrar may have been tight, teutonic and intolerant, but his panoramic view of hunger had helped the human condition and brought him deserved acclaim.

About this time there occurred yet another of the fluky connections that fashion the Borlaug saga. Both Harrar and Forrest ("Frosty") Hill, a Ford Foundation vice-president, happened to reside in Scarsdale. Both happened to ride the same commuter train from that tony New York suburb to their downtown offices, which were mere blocks apart. Both happened to be agriculture specialists, being the first in their separate institutions' leadership. Both also happened to be strong willed individualists, seemingly destined to be bitter rivals.

Yet both fell into friendship as fellow travelers on the train as well as on the road to a well-fed world. During commutes they often engaged in professional jawboning. One morning, George Harrar offered an opinion. "You know where it's most difficult to fill the food bowls?" he said. "Asia!"

This sparked an eager response — Frosty Hill had also been pondering Asia's food problem. "Why don't we go to the Philippines," he said, "and take a look around?"

Soon thereafter, the pooh-bah pair from powerful philanthropic establishments flew to Manila, and during a month of kibitzing decided to combine purses, powers and people to create a research center wherein large research teams could do for rice what a tiny team in Mexico had done for wheat.

The size difference seemed quite appropriate. Rice was this continent's most important food. Asians on average consumed more than 300 pounds a year, 50 times more than Westerners. The crop was so prominent and Asia so populous that even small research advances would ease existence for hundreds of millions. Moreover, rice is prone to collapse from adverse weather, not to mention myriad microbes and insects. Such collapses in the already hungry 1960s could be catastrophic, Asia's soaring population meant there were no reserves for rainy days, much less droughty decades.

Harrar and Hill proposed to rectify this by combining the talents of rice breeders, plant pathologists, soil scientists, and more – focusing them like a laser on the factors most limiting production.

In essence, this was a personal initiative of sympathetic subway straphangers. Both faced internal resistance because their foundations'

The International Rice Research Institute, Los Baños, 1961. Known worldwide as IRRI, this facility was the brainchild of the Ford and Rockefeller foundations and the Philippine government. It was created by to do for rice what Borlaug had done for wheat. The irony is that Borlaug's lean operation in Mexico was being closed while this lavish counterpart was being opened in the Philippines.

roots were anchored in fields of social gain rather than edible grain. Institutionally speaking, neither foundation was enamored by the idea of divesting so many dollars and investing so much distinction on an unprecedented venture of dubious prospect on the planet's dark side with a crop Americans barely knew and hadn't yet learned to love.

But together Harrar and Hill wielded enough clout to link the foundations and limn a unique agricultural venture at Los Baños, a university town an hour's drive south of Manila. Hill's foundation built the facilities; Harrar's foundation supported the staff and research activities. The Philippine government provided the site and certain services.

Unlike the little term-limited sideshow in Mexico, the new operation was set up as a grand, permanent, international institution working for every nation, solving any and all problems limiting production of this staple.

IRRI's inaugural director general, Robert Chandler, hailed from Maine and knew nothing of the tropics, let alone rice. But working with the Mexico program he'd caught the Borlaug bug. Thus he began with the aim of developing fast-maturing, disease-resisting dwarf rice plants that could hold up more grain than then seemed possible. He would also train a corps of rice cadets for Asian countries.

The rice work in Asia was thus an intellectual clone of Borlaug's pioneering efforts with wheat in Mexico.

Back there in Mexico fears were then rising over Norm's current best creation. Cajeme [cah-HEM-ee] 54 was capable of producing both exceptional yields and exceptional bread, but like other tall wheats it suffered from a weak stem. Sadly, after this plant fell down the grain tended to develop black tips.

Black coloration seriously scares cereal scientists because it can signify smut, a fungus that fills grains with black spores smelling like dead fish.

Norm pleaded with the farmers to limit the amount of fertilizer, so as to keep the heads from getting too heavy. But asking anyone to deliberately restrict the earnings from their labors goes against human nature. Cajeme 54 continued to get more nourishment than was good for it. Seeing the resulting stream of black grains Mexican millers screamed "Smut!" at the top of their leathery lungs.

This time the government threatened to take action. For Norm, the whole episode clung like a personal stain. And as a substitute he released Nainari 60 and urged the farmers to switch.

Though just as tall and just as high yielding, Nainari 60's stronger stem added an extra measure of wind resistance. Despite that, farmers only slowly switched to the safer substitute because it still required they limit fertilizer dosage. Taken all round, they preferred the devil they knew.

To test Nainari 60's outer limits Norm fenced in a small planting. Then with the plants physically incapable of falling over he used fertilizer to push them to their natural limit, which proved to be 3 *tons an acre*.

This was incredible. Allowed to fully express itself, this variety could lift Mexico's output by half again.

That insight cast into crystalline perspective the dwarf plants he's spent five years struggling to birth. Those half-pints can be pushed to their full potential with fertilizer but without fear and without fencing.

Those short, stiff-stemmed types are, however, still far off. And as the year 1961 comes to a close he's stuck with an ugly rumor that all his years of effort have merely yielded food that's unfit for human consumption.

1962

Perspectives

A S THE THIRD YEAR BEGINS Norm can survey the verdant Yaqui Valley and see his creations raising the roof over Sonora. This is no longer Mexico's Wild West. By putting down roots, thousands of wheat farmers are building up wealth. The sole concern is that both the uplift and the roof are sustained by the eight-year-old Cajeme 54, whose grain has a tendency to turn black.

In February the second batch of trainees descends on the Obregón City airport. Were you present this time you'd see young men from Cyprus, Egypt, Ethiopia, Iran, Iraq, Jordan, Libya, Pakistan, Syria, Saudi Arabia and Turkey. You'd also spot ten South Americans and a bevy of Mexicans whom Norm has invited on his own. These no-name pilgrims have come seeking enlightenment from the no-name mentor residing in this no-name town in a suncooked slice of nowhere.

From dawn to dusk during those springtime days of '62 the wheat plots at the CIANO experiment station echo the cheerful chatter of a motivated multinational work force measuring and recording in big screw-bound notebooks the vital details distinguishing wheat gems from wheat garbage.

This is a multi-purpose operation. Yes, they're training to be hunger fighters, but they're also perfecting the dwarf wheat; they're managing the plots that are outlier fields for American and Canadian wheat breeders whose home turf is hard frozen; and, by managing stem-rust tests, they're helping ensure the world's wheat is safe, reliable and immune to its worst foe.

During the April harvest period Glenn Anderson returns for his second foray into this hard-to-find hideaway. Again he's come to survey his countrymen's contributions, select the winners, and haul home the seeds for further advancement across the Prairie Provinces once snows allow.

Yet again Borlaug admired the big friendly Canuck who voluntarily stayed over and helped teach the students long after his counterparts had gathered their seeds and suitcases and scurried home. This time Norm took Anderson fishing along the irrigation canal and, by playing devil's advocate, plumbed the strength of his convictions. Years later he recalled:

> Glenn's drive to excel was impressive. He was impatient with mediocrity, lethargy, sloppy science, the status quo, and bureaucracy. I tucked all that away in the memory bank.
>
> I also provided him seed from our latest and best dwarf lines. They were not quite ready for use, but I figured Canadians would appreciate their short stiff straw. That was a unique factor and a basic advance of great commercial value. I figured that a nation that runs on wheat would be very excited.

As their final contribution hereabouts the cadet corps compiled the seed collections the U.S. Department of Agriculture disseminated to 50 locations around the world to confirm that Mexican and other wheats are immune to the entire spectrum of strains of the crop's most devastating diseases.

Just before sending the collection to Rody Rodenheiser in Washington Norm slipped in five envelopes containing experimental dwarf lines. The couple of hundred seeds in each envelope had been gathered from plants so pitiful any self-respecting wheat breeder should be embarrassed to let anyone see them. He merely wanted to learn how they'd weather the stem rust forces arrayed across the continents. He had no clue they'd provide the keys to the kingdom.

That April's harvest made clear that Sonora's farmers had once more over-fed Cajeme 54. Black-pointed grain was so prevalent the government began docking each ton of black grain 50 pesos (about $4).

Having contributed a million tons to the government supply, Sonora's farmers got docked a lot. Resentment festered until unrest bubbled up to society's surface like a boil. Hoping to lance that civic eruption, the agriculture ministry called a public meeting.

On that late-April Sunday morning representatives of every local farmer-organization gathered at the Yaqui Valley Farmer Cooperative Credit Union. The government agent proved to be a very hard nut.

Sánchez Cellis – brother to a notorious governor of Sinaloa, the state to the south – began by thundering that the black grain pouring onto the market constituted a national calamity. The farmers were to blame, they'd put on too much fertilizer. Despite regretting the penalty, he'd not reduce the amount a single peso. Smut, he said, was too serious.

During this dressing down the farmers sat with hunched shoulders; silent, depressed, demoralized. Norm felt that way too. Being the source of all this evil, he also felt disgrace.

Then Eva Villegas stepped to the podium. The previous week she and her colleague Federico Chacón had separated Cajeme 54 grains into groups of equal blackness: three-quarters, one-quarter, none at all. They'd then milled each group into flour and baked the separate flours into bread. Now, she passed the results around.

As the flour and bread samples went from hand to hand there was a tangible lightening of the tension. None possessed any unusual hue or odor . . . all were pure white and the bread smelled delicious.

For that there was but one explanation: the blackness had resided on the grain's outer skin and been milled away with the bran. That ruled out smut, whose black spores pervade the edible portion, resulting in gray flour and gray bread redolent of rotting fish.

A chastened government soon returned the millions it had withheld from the farmers' paychecks. More importantly for our story, Eva saved Norm from the charge of harming *both* farmer finances *and* consumer health.

By that fall the imperfect dwarfs that had defected in the denims departing from the 1960 Farmer Demonstration Day were trickling onto the market. Separately, Sonora's farmer co-ops and the Mexican government have multiplied seed for all. Ton lots for sowing the wheat zone are at hand.

Narvaez has named the pair Pitic [PIT-EEK] and Penjamo [pen-HAR-moe]. It was a big moment: the first release of commercial dwarf summer wheat. Pitic 62 and Penjamo 62 are waist high, with stems hefting heavy grain-filled heads. They have red-skinned grains. They yield 5870 lb an acre and they mature within 140 days. These are high-performance plants; too bad their seeds remain a miller's nightmare and their flour a baker's curse.

Of course the search for replacements goes on. For millers, the grain's center is being hardened; for bakers the gluten is being strengthened.

All that renovation is done in the dark dungeon inhabited by invisible

WHEAT APOSTLES, II . . .

The second group of trainees stands amid Pitic 62 and Penjamo 62. Wheat fields had been shoulder high until these shorties appeared. Both were big food producers. Pitic could yield 2.7 tons an acre; Penjamo 2.6. Moreover they were secure from the winds that had previously kept a lid on yield. Other than being abysmal breadmakers, they're great plants.

. . . CLASS OF '62

In addition to standing firm against the willful wind, these short plants convert more of the sun's energy and soil's nutrients into grain and less into straw and leaf tissue. The energy that would have built more stems and leaves was freed up to build more grain. As the saga continues the Pakistani, Nur Chaudry, and the Egyptian, El Ham Talaat, will play vital parts.

genes. A cluster of exciting possibilities is emerging gradually, painfully, but steadily as every likely possibility is milled and made into bread. During the harvest season, Borlaug hauls in hundreds of seed packets. Eva mills them into flour and bakes the flour into little loaves. The ease of milling and the height of the loaf determine whether that plant gets retained or rejected.

As head of quality control, she's too hardheaded to fall for any feelings he might fancy. She often trashes samples hosting his highest hopes. Should either the milling or the mini-loaves prove imperfect Eva marks them "unacceptable," and ends that line of advance.

One day in the fall of '62 she happened to be beside her laboratory at Chapingo outside Mexico City when Norm pranced down the path waving four seed packets. Her filing cabinet bulged with analyses made on the contents of similar packets he'd hauled in from the research fields on the 8000 foot high plateau at Toluca. But this time his manner seemed different. Instead of professional calmness, he radiated enthusiasm as he shouted:

> "Eva, aqui tenemos los mejores toros!" [Eva, here we have the best of the bulls!]

Norm, commonly talked up his genetic lines as if he was a cattle breeder, but she understood that this was the golden moment when the decade-long gambit with dwarfing genes might be about to pay off.

The six-year search for "short-straw" has required more than 8000 cross-pollinations. The particular seeds in the packets he's waving in the air came from progeny of the 8156th — a figure indicating their rarity and his resolution. From the 60 or so plants emerging from that magical 8156th gene blend he'd isolated four special standouts. Each was waist high. Each was disease resistant. Each was adapted to conditions as diverse as Toluca's moist sky-high mountainside and Sonora's bottom-dwelling desert. Moreover each produced multiple stems, each stem produced its own head of seed, and each seedhead produced almost twice the normal number of grains.

No wonder Norm pranced down the path that day at Chapingo. The seeds in these four packets represented his greatest masterpieces. Plants grown from these seeds feature every trait he'd sought. They could open horizons higher and wider than any cereal before. They can break the 3 ton per-acre-yield barrier.

But can they make good bread?

Everything rests on Eva's analysis.

CAREER SAVER #29

Fate's twenty-ninth facilitator, Eva Villegas saved Norm from being charged with harming both farmers' finances and human health. Now in her early thirties, the former student — who'd once tried to quit science to help out her impoverished mother — now determines which of the research plots' best performing plants will advance. In her cramped and rickety lab she turns the grain into bread. From thousands of samples, only a rare few the tests get Eva's approval. She is the gatekeeper to all that later transpires.

Norm could by now exert influence in nine countries where he has pre-positioned fifth-columns of young hunger fighters. Nonetheless, the most perilous country in the most populous continent remains stubbornly beyond reach. India refuses to send a single soul to Mexico. It doesn't need help, thank you very much.

The breakthrough happened inadvertently. When Rody Rodenheiser mailed out the thimbles of seed for the 1962 International Stem-Rust Nursery a few grams of Borlaug's five embarrasingly bad experimental dwarfs reached India's capital of New Delhi.

India was then humanity's basketcase. Cereals supplied 90 percent of the diet, and the total harvest (wheat, rice, corn, sorghum and millet) of almost 50 million tons had to feed 450 million citizens. Theoretically, therefore, no one could access more than 230 lb a year. As people need 730 lb of grain a year, Indians were getting barely a fifth of biological requirement.

Put another way, although people need 2 lb of grain daily, Indians were getting only 10 ounces. This was a starvation ration, and it was declining as the number of mouths climbed by nearly a million a month.

Only American generosity kept India from starving. The New Delhi government operated a vast system that unloaded U.S. grain in a dozen ports and sent it throughout the sprawling nation of over a million square miles. There, more than 50,000 "Fair Price Shops" passed out sacks of grain to more than 100 million poor.

This giant life-saving operation – probably history's largest neighborly food rescue – was a great success. After almost a decade, however, it was spawning unintended consequences that it became no success at all.

For one thing, millions of the poor were forced to fast when, as happened not infrequently, a ship got delayed and the shops stayed shut.

For another, the U.S. government eventually held a third of India's money supply, having literally bought the country with free food.

Worst of all, Indian farmers had quit striving to grow extra food. Unable to compete against the Fair Price Shops they gave up. Local production as a consequence sagged just as the need soared.

Strange to say, India was a country of farmers. Sad to say, it was also a sluggish socialist state wherein farmers counted for little in the national priority list. The national leadership considered the notions of competition, market forces and profits to be heretical. Decisions were made by a central command that meant well but mistook the needs of the moment. National priorities emphasized heavy industries, nuclear advancement, and international eminence.

The two-thirds of the people engaged in agriculture were blocked from access to credit, free markets or information. Getting loans required an elaborate, lengthy, bureaucratic trial of endurance to prove income, land ownership and crop yields from the preceding five years. Moreover, farmers were required to sell their grain to government middlemen. And the government paid as little as possible on the basis that the poor should get cheap bread.

None of this could be changed by the will of the majority. Politically, India was a dictatorship in democratic camouflage. Its founding father, Jawaharlal Nehru and his Congress Party had led, almost unchallenged, since Independence in 1947. During that decade and a half Nehru had flirted with communal farming, communist tractors and Stalinist five-year plans centered around the false belief that India had a strong and secure rural base from which to build steel mills.

Though in international relations he posited a policy of nonalignment, he idolized the command economy of the Soviet Union, a country barely capable of feeding its people. Worse, he fostered testy relations with the United States, the one country willing to release food for rupees.

Despite an inability to feed its citizens India's government devoted about 30 percent of the national budget to defence. That hit was huge for a country forever running out of foreign exchange. Though some of the military materiel was American, most of India's quality currency was wasted buying Soviet weapons.

Behind the all-powerful bureaucracy stood an all-powerful political body that stamped its will without accounting to the electorate. Even cabinet ministers could not override the much feared Planning Commission, let alone make major decisions without its prior approval. And this government within a government of a food-short, famine-prone peasant society was focused gimlet-eyed on industrialization, armaments and heavy industries.

But by 1962 food shortages were undermining collective confidence in the country's trajectory, not to mention leadership. With fear of hunger forever at their elbows, millions were angry and fearful; insecurity had become a national trait.

Contributing also to insecurity was India's testy relations with its

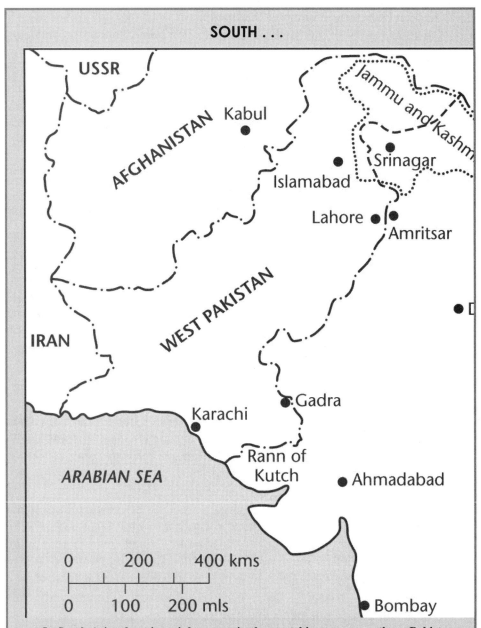

SOUTH . . .

USSR

AFGHANISTAN   Kabul

Jammu and Kashm

Srinagar

Islamabad

IRAN

WEST PAKISTAN

Lahore

Amritsar

Gadra

Karachi

Rann of
Kutch

ARABIAN SEA

Ahmadabad

| 0 | 200 | 400 kms |

| 0 | 100 | 200 mls |

Bombay

In South Asia wheat is mainly grown in the stretching across northern Pakistan and north India in a generally west-east direction. One of the world's most productive areas, it provides both countries with a large part of their food. It lies at about the same latitude as Houston, Texas. The "Pakistan" this book deals with was then called West Pakistan.

... ASIA

— · — INTERNATIONALLY-RECOGNISED BORDE

— — — DISPUTED BORDERS

· · · · · · · STATE OF JAMMU AND KASHMIR

Kashmir

CHINA

Lhasa

Tibet

NEPAL

BHUTAN

Delhi

Katmandu

Kanpur

EAST PAKISTAN

Dacca

Calcutta

INDIA

BAY OF BENGAL

The northern lowlands – stretching eastwards for 2000 miles from the Indus River to the Ganges Delta – constitute a great alluvial plain. There, Pakistan grew 15 million acres of wheat; India 35 million acres. Most was grown in the plains of Punjab and the upper Ganges.

neighbor Pakistan, which at that time straddled India on both sides.

Just 15 years before, they'd been a one nation under several gods. Then in 1947 Britain had given up trying to keep the quarrelsome factions together and walked away, leaving the inhabitants to sort themselves into a Hindu-majority nation (India) and a Moslem-majority nation (Pakistan). The separation was messy, not to say murderous, and fifteen years later the social scars refuse to heal. Each nation resents the other over the question of which should control Kashmir. As a result, they share little but a boundary. Their citizens never visit each other. There's neither mail nor airline service. Telephone connections are sporadic. Cablegrams may take weeks to move a few miles.

With roughly a third of India's population, Pakistan produced about a third as much wheat. The western province – today's nation of Pakistan – included the vast basin of the Indus River, which flows south from the Himalayas more than a thousand miles to the sea at Karachi. Wheat was its main crop. Pakistanis like Indians lived on flat bread known as naan, roti or chapatties.

Pakistan was pro-Western and a friend of the U.S. It too is getting American grain shipments. Of its 100 million people, roughly 85 million are farmers. Agriculture generated about half the nation's annual wealth, which obviously was abysmal considering that the average rural income was barely $60 per person per year.

About the only thing the two nations shared was dependence on the monsoon. One of the world's most intense regular weather events, it delivers up to 90 percent of a year's rainfall. Monsoon rains normally began falling in June and for the next four months shape the lives of Indians and Pakistanis. Their moisture fed agriculture, which in turn fed more than half a billion souls, and those in turn fed the economy and made the countries progress.

Sadly, though, the world's most intense regular weather event is not all that regular. Some years it delivers the farmers their blessed liquid manna from heaven. Some years it delivers floods that sweep away crops and communities. Some years it fails, leaving plants and people stricken and starving.

This is how things stood that October day when the few grams of seed of Borlaug's embarrasingly bad experimental dwarfs reached India's capital of New Delhi. All life depends on this fickle arbitrator of sustenance and starvation. The U.S. is staving off famine while Indians denounce America to the world. God-rich India is building nuclear capacity and military might with the help of godless Soviets. And the two impoverished neighbors making up most of this traditionally pacific part of the world are arming themselves for mutually assured destruction.

No one knew the dozen or so seeds in each of the five packets were anything special. Indeed, to most observers the resulting plants were living horrors of the cereal world. As we've said, Borlaug had sent them solely to see if they could withstand the strains of rust disease hereabouts. He should have been ashamed.

The one who saw them as keys to the Kingdom was Momkombu Sambasivan Swaminathan [swah-mee-NAH-than]. Then 38 and a cytogeneticist at the Indian Agricultural Research Institute in New Delhi, he'd already concluded that stem weakness and stem rust were the main suppressors of his country's food supply. On spying the four outliers, he was intrigued by their smallness, their stem strength and their immunity to stem rust, which was then plaguing India. Peering intently at the 50 or so plants through his rather thick spectacles he suddenly saw the possibility of leapfrogging India's famine.

He immediately sent an invitation to Borlaug to visit India's wheat-lands and give his advice.

It was the beginning of the mend.

A s autumn approaches, Agriculture Canada's research fields near Winnipeg are looking stunning. Glenn Anderson watches them with amazement. Borlaug's partially perfected dwarfs are besting his country's best. Indeed, by season's end, they'd surpassed the local elites by 25 percent.

Though this foreshadowed a food and financial windfall for a wheat-dependent economy, opposition arose swift and sure. The Canadian Wheat Board declared the gluten too weak and banned the grain from exports. That was all it took to kill the initiative. After that, no farmer could afford to sow Borlaug seed, and the chance to raise the roof over Canada was deferred.

Soon thereafter Norm learned that no American company had even sown the seed samples Don Fletcher passed out from his office in Minneapolis. Nothing from Mexico, they thought, could be worth that much trouble.

In Mexico City late in the year Eva Villegas made her pronouncement: the special short-straw strains – the four selections from the 8156th cross-pollination carrying Norm's highest hopes – *were indeed great breadmakers!*

From this endorsement, will come Borlaug's fifth and most famous wheat generation. He urged the seed be immediately bulked up and supplied to farmers across Mexico's northern, drier, wheat-growing tier. But Nacho Narvaez worried about a stem rust variant in the lower and more humid sections of Mexico. That fungal variant possessed the power to infect two of these four. He and the Mexican leadership felt that these two – the best of the four – should be held back.

This fear will pointlessly delay production of that pair for two years.

That in turn will open the gate for a wily farmer to undertake the initiative on his own.

And that in its turn will change the course of history.

But as 1962 comes to a close no one can even imagine such an unprecedented happening.

1963
Pivot

THE FOURTH YEAR OPENS with Norm fully absorbed in Rockefeller Foundation responsibilities. In a life as turbulent as the tides this is a slack-water interlude, and he has reason for satisfaction: the days of disorder are behind; the quiet life of a teacher is ahead; his wheat progeny are around.

Those progeny extending on all sides represent history's first large scale crop of dwarf summer wheat. They lend the Yaqui Valley the look of a patchwork quilt, with a few fields of the old five-footers standing tall amid expanses of the new three footers, Petic 62 and Penjamo 62. Since being sown two months ago, the shorties have been fully fertilized. Not until March, however, will the wicked winds huff and puff and try to blow them down. Only then will anyone know for certain whether halving stems doubles yield.

Borlaug, it should be said, is far too busy to stare at the scenery. He's perfecting substitutes that both unleash wheat's full genomic strength *and* meet general milling and baking standards. He's managing research plots as a gift to snowbound colleagues in Canada and the U.S. He's maintaining myriad observation plots for interest, for insight and for intrigue. He's working to shrink pasta wheat and triticale, which are quite separate but complementary cereals. And beyond such sidelines he's performing his proper profession: training agronomic acolytes, who this year have come from Argentina, Cyprus, Egypt, Ethiopia, Iran, Iraq, Jordan, Pakistan, Syria, and Turkey.

Then into all that banter, bustle and bedlam dropped Swaminathan's letter. Norm had never considered helping India, but, despite guilt over deserting his duty, he bought a ticket. The clincher came when John Gibler (who'd helped make the first dwarf wheat cross-pollinations seven years back) offered to run the show while he's gone.

By March he's winging eastward on his second trip beyond the Americas' comforting confines. While Pan Am's unbelievably huge new jet – a Boeing 707 – thrusts him into the maelstrom of mass hunger, he's quite unaware he's heading for his life's signature battlefront. Amazingly, there's no formal plan, fancy budget, formalized meetings or fiscal proprieties; just a no-name climbing into a plane in the capital of Mexico in response to a letter from a no-name half a world away in the capital of India.

At the New Delhi airport he finds the Rockefeller Foundation's local director. An experienced soil scientist and agronomist, Ralph Cummings is a paragon of reserve and southern courtesy. A decade earlier the Rockefeller Foundation dispatched this gentle North Carolinian to Delhi to shake up India's moribund agriculture. Subsequently he'd helped erect two universities modeled on America's Land Grant agricultural colleges. In contrast to the British style worship of theory and academic achievement, these disgorge doers devoted to dirt farming and disentangling food-production problems. Just what India needs.

Following a session with Swaminathan, Norm headed out for a month's immersion in India's wheatlands. His timing was terrific; the Ganges Plain was abuzz with people preparing to harvest wheat. But this trek – much like one he'd made across rural Mexico in 1945 – stirred the blood. Here was reflected the same hard agronomy Julius Caesar's serfs decried. Grain was harvested by sickle and handled in sacks. Yields were measured by quintal (112 lb), and were typically 7 quintals an acre, which pinned millions of families on poverty's edge.

All this was reminiscent of his boyhood days before the Midwest underwent its magnificent makeover. Absent high-performing crops, four out of ten rural Indians lived on less than 10 cents (50 Naye Paise) a day. Absent cash, they had to fashion lives out of nothing, and dwelt in mud-walled huts without sanitation or running water. Absent electricity, they cooked over smoky fires fueled with sundried cow dung. Absent public transportation, they were literally marooned for life. Absent schools or a teacher, they couldn't improve their lot, let alone their childrens' lots.

These sights were especially horrifying because Norm had just left the Yaqui Valley, which shares latitude, climate and conditions with India's northern plains and the valleys along the Himalayan foothills, where most of the wheat is grown. Sonora's farmers were preparing for the harvest too, but come April each acre of Petic 62 and Penjamo

62 was expected to produce more than 50 quintals (3 tons). Such an amount was far too big for sickles, and for six years Sonora farmers have been using combine harvesters, heavy trucks and bulk handling.

Norm's dilemma was how to make India's dysfunctional agriculture just like Mexico's newly functional one.

Some possibilities were plain to see:

Better soils. Worn out by continual cultivation, soils were weak and weakening further with every harvest. Yet nothing was being done to restore nutrients. Fertilizers were essentially unknown; everyone declared them far too expensive for farmers so poor.

Better plants. Most of the fields contained mixtures of mediocre wheats incapable of producing even moderate yields. For three decades the annual average had remained stuck at a seemingly impenetrable ceiling of 800 pounds an acre. Norm noticed too that the plants were peppered with stem rust and were too tall for their own good, not to mention human good.

Better policies. Bureaucracy's iron hand was clamped vice-like on the two-thirds of Indians who, without access to credit, free markets or information, were supposed to cultivate their country's food. They also were required to sell their grain to government middlemen who deliberately underpaid so city folk could enjoy cheap bread.

Better professionals. Though India had 10,000 college graduates in agriculture, those Norm met seemed unconcerned over their nation's plight. Most saw their jobs as entitlements.

At different stops he suffered through seemingly endless excuses for research that was going nowhere and was incapable of lifting hunger's haunting shadow from the land. Most were engaged in what he scornfully called "splinter programs," "scientific sideshows," or "chasing academic butterflies."

Again, the sight of agricultural scientists accepting paychecks while ignoring their hungry clients and the need for speed disgusted him. The only thing that disgusted him more was their excuses:

> When I asked about the need to modernize agriculture, both scientists and administrators typically replied, "Poverty is the farmers' lot; they are used to it."
>
> I was even informed that the farmers were proud of their lowly status, and was assured that they wanted no change.
>
> After my own experiences in Iowa and Mexico I didn't believe a word of it.

CAREER SAVER #30

Fate's thirtieth facilitator, Ralph Cummings. The Rockefeller Foundation field director for India, he funded the creation of agricultural universities, modeled on U.S. Land Grant colleges. Those and their graduates will help spearhead the introduction of Borlaug's wheats into India. Cummings also brought Borlaug's wheats to the attention of India's agriculture minister Chidambara Subramaniam. And in time he'll pay for large amounts of Mexican wheat seed to be imported into India.

This was a food supply with only echoes of the ancient past and no hope of a future. But, given the pervasive pessimism, paralysis and smug acceptance of the status quo, introducing any alternative would be a challenge. Doubt dominated all discussions about the food supply and the future. Cynicism also led to widespread indifference to science throughout the society. Not even the scientists were confident of the product they peddled.

Norm saw that the system was crushing the soul out of India's food production system. The farmers didn't have a chance:

> I came out of that tour certain that whatever we provided, the farmers could never make a change by themselves. Before a wheat revolution could get off the ground issues reaching all the way to the top of the government had to be settled.

He also saw that, though not a hopeful place, rural India was far from hopeless. Many technical possibilities had not been tried. Indeed, he could virtually touch the new future that was out beyond the old. But to get there someone had to raise the sights and broaden the vision of empty headed authorities who ignored the need for speed.

He decided to begin right away. In addressing a group of administrators and scientists in the city of Kanpur, he made four predictions:

- In a few years India will double or triple wheat production;
- Demand for fertilizer will skyrocket;
- Cultivation practices will change beyond recognition; and
- The country will have difficulty handling the harvest!

They all thought me quite mad.

Only in Punjab [puhn-JARB] did he sense a promising window to the wider future. The name means "land of five rivers," and it designates a broad, fat and fertile expanse extending across the Indus and Ganges headwaters. One of the supposed cradles of civilization, the great Punjab Plain gets only about a foot of rain a year and was near-desert until the 1930s when British engineers installed vast irrigation works. Only then did people settle in numbers and turn it into India's breadbasket.

Norm liked the Punjabi farmers. They still possessed the pioneering spirit. Like his friends the Yaqui Valley farmers, they seemed a scrappy lot, shrinking neither from a stranger nor a silly question. Above

RURAL INDIA . . .

In his tour of India's wheat zone in 1963 Borlaug saw scenes like this. To us, it may seem quaint, but he could see many things wrong. The plants were low yielding. The stands are thin because the soil was worn out. Harvesting by hand involved tremendous toil for a few hundred pounds of grain. Water was pumped laboriously by animals walking in circles. This was farming for subsistence, not money. Workers like these got paid in grain. The distribution was not always equitable but it kept them alive for a while.

. . . BEFORE BORLAUG

Seeing a crop harvested by hand Norm back to the horrors of picking corn when he was small. He later said, "It gave me an undying admiration for the women in Third-World countries who do such things every day, many of them from the age of seven until they succumb at an early age to overwork." People like these seemed content, but he knew that that was only because they'd never seen anything better. This whole scene reflected the agriculture of the ancients; it was too inefficient to sustain modern India's soaring population.

all, they seemed committed to bettering themselves.

In the years right ahead, Borlaug and Punjabi farmers will make an unbeatable team. But for the moment all he's aware of is the joy in finding farmers who, amid all the doom and doubt, were enthusiastic, hard-working, skilled and determined.

He also found the same spirit among a small cadre of scientists. These outliers exhibited calmness, strength and foresight, and sought to solve the food problem, not merely study it. They were principally centered in the Indian Agricultural Research Institute (IARI) in New Delhi and the Punjab Agricultural University and Pantnagar University – all three institutions being modeled on American land grant colleges and staffed with doers devoted to dirt farming and disentangling food-production problems.

The day before he'd head homeward, Norm was guest of honor at a luncheon at that institute in New Delhi. Present in that small room in the library building were a dozen food and agriculture specialists.

Friendly, competent, optimistic, they were eager to hear his views. They saw the country's needs in strategic terms and were propelled by the urgency of the situation. This small group included Swaminathan, who headed the IARI's division of genetics, and B.P. Pal, who headed its graduate school.

High expectation enlivened the scene as Norm elaborated on the types of people he'd met during his month of immersion:

> *The agricultural researchers.* They are not contributing enough; too many are merely holding down a job, striving for academic laurels or wasting their time on scientific sideshows.
>
> *The politicians.* They are treating the farmer unfairly by not properly rewarding his effort. That is self-defeating because the farmer's the guy who grows the food. You can't play fast and loose with his faith; he must know the score and feel confident about his future. He must also be adequately compensated for his labors.
>
> *The farmers.* They are much more capable than anyone is crediting. They can achieve big advances. They're not conservative; they're not happy with their lot; they don't like their present situation. Give them a chance and they will respond and the food supply will strengthen out of sight.

Finally Swaminathan raised the issue of the moment: "Now that you've seen all this," he asked, "do you think your wheats could do for India what they've done for Mexico?"

CAREER SAVER #31

Fate's thirty-first facilitator, M.S. Swaminathan. A plant geneticist who became a driving force behind the introduction of Mexican wheats to India, Swaminathan was the first to grasp the possibilities of Borlaug's work. After spotting some of the compact Mexican plants in a test plot near New Delhi, he invited Borlaug to visit. That trip began everything, and he was one of the few in the world who could see potential in the defective plants that should have embarrassed Borlaug.

As a child, Swaminathan had seen Mahatma Gandhi attend political meetings at his parents' home. This had a considerable influence on him. And after the 1942-43 famine, when several million Indians perished, he was determined to do what he could to prevent such a shocking tragedy ever being repeated.

He might at first glance seem an unlikely person through whom to understand the Asian transition from a traditional to a modernizing agriculture. A competent scientist and a devout Hindu, he was pleasant, open, soft-spoken, congenial and respectful both of the Western world and India's heritage.

At a moment of very high ideological fervor in his country he remained non-ideological and committed to practical reality, commonsense and scientific truth. Through these qualities he steered the modernization of his country's agriculture.

Silence descended. Borlaug sensed the group willing him to pull from his pocket the final solution to India's food situation:

> They were hoping I'd declare our wheats capable of transplanting the whole Mexican experience into India. I could not give them this assurance. I wasn't at all sure. Caution was necessary. "There are imponderables," I said; "we just don't know enough yet."

The spirit that had energized the room deflated like a balloon with a stickpin. But Borlaug was far from downcast:

> The fact that India had never sent anyone for training meant that the only experience to go by was the few disfigured plants in Swaminathan's plots. That was too small a sample to tell anything.
> But I was thinking of the two young trainees, Nur Chaudry and Mansur Bajawa next door in Pakistan, and El Ham Talaat who worked at a station north of Cairo, Egypt. By now, they would have meaningful results.
> I smiled at Swaminathan. "On my way home I can find out the things we need to know," I said. "Give me a few weeks and I'll write you a report answering the question."

Mansur Bajwa and Nur Chaudry worked at Pakistan's main agricultural research institute in the town then called Lyallpur. Norm anticipated slipping in quietly and seeing them in private. The country's agriculture secretary, however, had arranged a special field day in his honor. Thus, he reached the Ayub Khan Research Institute to find a host of civil servants, researchers, reporters, and a scattering of westerners awaiting his arrival. Even the agriculture secretary had motored down the 70 miles from Lahore.

It was the eve of his 50th birthday, and would prove one of his worst days:

> Following formal greetings and ritual cups of tea the throng trooped out behind the administration building to inspect the side-by-side rows of Mexican and Pakistani wheats.
> Addressing the gathered host, the institute director turned the occasion into a tribute to his own work. He made a big hit. All the viewers were nodding; Pakistani plants were strong and productive. That was obvious.
> Then Anwar Hussain turned toward the Mexican wheats. "These don't fit in Pakistan," he declared. "See how inferior they are."
> Turning to me, he said almost apologetically: "Dr. Borlaug, your

varieties aren't well adapted here." His sorrow seemed genuine . . . seeing I'd come so far to find disappointment.

But that was not how I saw things. "WHAT IN THE HELL IS GOING ON HERE?" I yelled loud enough so no one could miss the message. "You didn't plant them properly. They're too far apart. And you haven't fed these damn things . . . They haven't been properly fertilized. And no weeding has been done!"

That took the administrator aback; he'd probably never been challenged on his home turf – certainly not so bluntly nor before his boss or his country's press. However he replied respectfully but forcefully: "Dr. Borlaug, this is the way wheat *must* be grown in Pakistan. See how beautiful our own varieties are!"

By now I was losing my grip: "The agronomy is all wrong," I stammered. "You didn't fertilize enough. You planted them too deep and got a poor stand. Everything is wrong. No one can tell anything from these tests."

"Sir," the director said loudly and with finality, "THIS IS THE WAY YOU PLANT WHEAT IN PAKISTAN!"

During the following hours, which were devoted to showcasing the station's own success, Norm insisted to whomever he could button-hole that there'd been a miscarriage of science, maybe justice. His plants had not only been badly handled they'd been abused:

Over and over I kept repeating my message. "Twenty years of targeted research lie behind these wheats. With them, Mexico went from hunger to self-sufficiency in 12 years. Pakistan can do the same thing. In fact, you can do it faster!"

But the words echoed hollow. The evidence was exposed for anyone with eyes; in Pakistan, Mexican plants were just plain losers.

As the afternoon wore on, Norm noticed a small owlish man wearing thick-rimmed glasses standing in the background sedulously scribbling notes with a stubby pencil. It was not a happy sight:

He seemed like a reporter, and I foresaw a big bold headline:
PAKISTAN'S WHEAT SURPASSES MEXICO'S.
What a depressing thought. Years would pass before we could overcome so public a setback.

Also standing in the background were his two young colleagues. Both Mansur Bajwa and Nur Chaudry were strangely silent, almost frozen. Something in their stance told the story:

They'd clearly been marginalized. Trying to improve wheat in

Pakistan was a lost cause. I gave up arguing and, after a miserable afternoon under the blistering sun, was hustled off to the institute's guesthouse for chicken curry served with all the pleasantries.

During the meal the agriculture secretary, sitting beside me, was friendly and, despite the day's revelations, seemed far from discouraged. With him, I continued pressing the case. However, Malik Khuda Bakhsh Bucha made clear he was no scientist; indeed his grace and charm made him seem shallow and superficial. It was not encouraging. And at the end I couldn't tell if he believed me or his own eyes.

Rigid scheduling left no chance to talk privately with the young trainees. But following the dinner, just as he was being hustled toward the exit, the two sidled over. "We've got something to show you in the morning," they said.

He explained he'd be leaving at ten; there'd be no time to meet.

"We'll come at dawn," they whispered.

As Borlaug fled the dining hall, the scribe who'd stood scribbling in the background extended a hand. "Haldore Hanson," he said.

While they ambled toward the institute guesthouse, Norm noticed his enormous briefcase, thick enough for a pile of books, maybe a bottle.

Hanson was smallish, slim and serious. His strong, almost molded, face featured thick gray brows and a winning smile. In Borlaug's room he seized the carafe of boiled water, and soon was thrusting forward a liberally enlivened glass: "I wrote down all you said this afternoon," he explained. "I don't know much about agriculture but you seem to think your wheats can make a difference. Did I hear you right? Is a big lift in food production possible in Pakistan?"

Borlaug stared over the rim of his glass: "Basically, you heard correctly. That fruit is just waiting to be picked. Data from the plantings you saw today will show Mexican wheats to be inferior, but that's only because they were mishandled."

Hanson took another sip of scotch and peered intently and said, "We have some talking to do."

Rather than a reporter, Hanson was the local Ford Foundation program director. Since 1962 he'd supported education and family planning (his wife called him "The Contraceptive Wallah"). His foundation had *never* run an agricultural development project. Yet because nine out of ten Pakistanis were farmers, he was keen to help.

Hanson's main fear was that his bosses back in the Big Apple would argue that their foundation lacked the technical expertise. Norm told him not to worry:

> "We'll gladly work with you," I said. "Between the Rockefeller Foundation and the Mexican Institute of Agriculture we've got the technical staff, the seeds, the scientific know-how. We can provide these, and train more Pakistanis as well."
>
> Strictly speaking, I had no authority to commit the Rockefeller Foundation to a Pakistan program. But I'm sure glad I did.

On this, one of the darkest of days Hal Hanson's confidence shone as the single bright spot. That anyone might support plants whose inferiority had been made so plain came as a huge relief. The next day would, however, provide a second bright spot:

> I tried desperately to sleep that night. My mind was in turmoil. I'd promised to send the Indians an answer, but what could I say? Here in Pakistan Mexican wheats looked awful. Should I tell Swaminathan that? Would he trust me or would he trust the research data that seemed so damning?
>
> At the moment when dawn was breaking a tapping on the window brought me out of a fitful doze. I slid back the curtain to see Bajwa and Chaudry standing in the gloom. Quickly I pulled on work clothes and boots. The three of us crossed the dewy lawns, wordlessly wending our way in single file down the tracks between experimental plots to an area beyond.
>
> It was all very mysterious until the two stepped aside and I could see four green plots, each roughly the dimension of a bowling lane. Although they carried no labels or nameplates, I immediately knew who they were.
>
> In the grainy light of a Punjab dawn those four Mexican varieties stood as strong and as heavy with seed as in the Yaqui Valley. This was perhaps the greatest sight of my career. It was so captivating I could have danced.
>
> Bajwa and Chaudry seemed delighted too. We shook hands; we laughed; we knelt and peered closely at those wonderful friends. We all knew they foreshadowed something great.
>
> For me this came as a revelation. The cobwebs of doubt were instantly swept away. Everything I'd dreamed of finding was there before me. Now I had something definite to tell Swaminathan: *Mexico's experiences could indeed be replicated on this side of the world!*

Not until several days later did Norm recall that it had been his 50th birthday, and concluded he couldn't have gotten a better present.

CAREER SAVER #32

Fate's thirty-second facilitator, Haldore Hanson. Director of the Ford Foundation Pakistan program, he had no experience with agriculture but decided to back Borlaug despite a disastrous demonstration. The success in Pakistan was especially due to his brilliant use of written communications. He deployed reports not only to document progress but also to move people's hearts and minds. No visiting consultant ever left Pakistan without first submitting a written summary of what had been seen and done, and what actions were required to keep the program moving ahead. "You have to brand when the iron is hot," he said to them all.

There remained, however, a riddle. And he remembered raising it with Bajwa and Chaudry:

Why didn't you grow the whole breeding nursery like this?
He wouldn't let us.
Who wouldn't let you?
The Director of Research!

The trainees' insubordination mirrored Borlaug's own beliefs about dealing with a boss's bad decision. Their Mexican training officially suppressed, the pair had secretly kept aside some seeds, planted them where no one would notice, omitted all labels, and cared for the plants in the proper manner. It was an act of immense courage; had they been caught their careers would have ended. Agricultural scientists in Pakistan had only one possible employer: government.

At Egypt's main wheat breeding station at Giza Borlaug found not only El Ham Talaat but a repeat performance. As they stood almost in the shadow of the Sphinx, yet another pompous research director declared Mexican plants inferior.

The plots bore that out, but Norm could see that once more a trainee had been forced to conform to his director's demands. The undernourished Mexican plants had fallen far short of their potential.

At the very instant Norm was about to uncork a storm of protest he noticed Talaat's face:

The young man seemed agonized. I sensed that further revelations were to come, so I held my tongue. Sure enough, next day Talaat drove me 60 miles north to a small experiment station at Sakha in the Nile Delta. There, he'd grown several plots exactly as we did in Mexico. Those looked as beautiful as any I'd ever seen.

Relieved in mind and restored in spirit, Borlaug hurried home. He was on Pan Am's famous Flight 001, which flew westbound around the world. As it droned over the Atlantic between Shannon and Gander he sat through the night, wide awake. His stream of consciousness was a rushing torrent that kept repeating: This thing can go! It can really take off!

His arrival in Sonora coincided with the harvest. For a month the wicked winds have huffed and puffed and the prodigal dwarfs Petic 62 and Penjamo 62 still hold their heavy heads high.

Sadly, he had no time to savor the thrill. The coming days were spent in the sweat of each moment: helping the trainees deal with the data pouring in from CIANO's research plots; helping document the breeding nurseries' results; and helping manhandle the harvest.

Only one incident marred that month of highs: a blaze broke out in the tinder-dry, end-of-season plants. Several acres of seed-increase plantings went up in smoke. Norm had long feared a field fire. But this one could have been much worse: the flames refrained from devouring the research plots. Thank goodness for that – losing those unique gene combos might have negated much that would eventually raise the roof over humanity.

Nights that April were spent holed up in the Costa de Oro where he could think and write. Despite tired brain and tired muscles, sleep wouldn't come; Swaminathan and his colleagues in New Delhi needed his report. Each evening he retired for a hot bath followed by a pen-and-paper session with his mind and its magnificent new vision.

In the loneliness of that motel room he pondered all he'd seen in six weeks. Sonora seemed like paradise. On the back of a few high-performance plants food was filling silos reaching toward the skies. That year the harvest would approach 2 million tons. Production had risen for 11 straight years — an indication that it was based neither on coincidence nor climate. And the latest spike was due to the still smallish area planted to the pair of dwarfs with defective DNA.

Two decades back, this rural magnificence had mirrored the rural misery he'd seen in Asia. Obviously, India and Pakistan needn't go hungry; their farmers needn't remain impoverished.

His 20-page reply to Swaminathan opened with an explanation of what he'd seen in Pakistan and Egypt. Later pages expressed his confidence that India could double her wheat harvest. In part they said:

> The evidence at this time is circumstantial; but fragmentary as it is, there is the prospect of a spectacular breakthrough in grain production for India. The new Mexican varieties that I have seen growing incline me to say that they will do well in India and grow beautifully. But though such opportunities do exist, there are conditions that must be met with fact and action — and not with

talk and probability. If the disease resistance holds up in its present spectrum — and we can check that quickly — and if the quantities of fertilizer and other vital necessities are made available, then there is a chance that something big could happen.

Then came a caution:

I must warn, however, that senior scientists and administrators must not hold this thing in check and must not restrict the ardor of the bright young scientists. If they do this, they will cause roadblocks and bottlenecks for which the poor will pay the price in continued hunger.

Finally, he damned the professionals' preoccupation with sideshows.

They are mostly chasing academic butterflies, and that is distracting them from what needs to be done to solve the hunger problem.

Although happy with the language, Norm hated the look. In their ignorance of English, CIANO's secretaries had liberally littered typos throughout. What could he do about that? Too clumsy fingered to manage a typewriter and bone weary from dawn-to-dark days in hot dusty fields, he passed the buck:

In the end I decided to hell with waiting, and mailed the crude manuscript to Ralph Cummings with a note: "Please get this edited and retyped before sending it on to Drs. B.P. Pal and M.S. Swaminathan."
The Rockefeller Foundation office in New Delhi had English-speaking typists, and I felt sure someone there would soften my blunt language and drop my most offensive charges. In particular, I expected them to remove my hot and hasty comment about academic butterflies, which would anger Indian scientists no end.

In a similar letter dispatched to Pakistan's secretary of agriculture, he apologized for the bad spelling and told Malik Khuda Bakhsh that his counterparts in India were likely to inject money and Mexican seeds into their wheat research and production efforts.

It was his first attempt to prick national pride and play the sides off against each other so as to ratchet up food production in both.

When the Sonora harvest was finally completed Norm prepared separate sets of seeds. Each contained small samples gathered from 225 of that season's best performers, including some from the still-developing 8156 dwarf generation. Then for the set destined for India, he added 250 lb each of what would later be named Lerma Rojo 64, Sonora 64 and Mayo 64. And for the set going to Pakistan he included 250 lb each of the future Sonora 64 and Mayo 64.

Although the shipments together weighed over half a ton he paid Pan Am to fly them to South Asia. It took a small fortune but there was no other way to assure their arrival before the next sowing deadline in December.

Borlaug thus reached a supremely satisfying point of his life. He'd completed his responsibility to South Asia. Now he could return to his proper job of training young agriculturists in Mexico:

> I saw no need for further involvement. My active participation in Pakistan and India was over. Their scientists now had good seed. They could carry on by themselves.

During the summer that followed, Mexico's president hosted a state dinner to formally close out the Rockefeller Foundation connection with Mexican agriculture. The function was held downtown in the capital and the president was scheduled to recognize the achievements of the collaborators who since the dark days of 1943 had transformed the local production of wheat, corn and potatoes.

However, when Adolfo López Mateos reached the rostrum he raised a quite unexpected topic: "I've just returned from a trip to Southeast Asia," he said, "and in the Philippines the president insisted I inspect the wonderful new international rice research institute. It was fascinating to see all those beautiful fields and laboratory buildings. And when I was ready to leave, the institute's director said, 'Mr. President, of course you know that all this had its roots back in Mexico with the joint program between the Rockefeller Foundation and the Mexican government.'

"I was impressed. And now I want to see the work you have done go forward. I want to see established *here in Mexico* an international institute like that one in the Philippines. In this case it can focus on maize [corn] and wheat. We the people of Mexico will invite students from other developing countries to come study with us, and in doing so we can repay in part the pioneering program we're saying goodbye to here tonight. We cannot finance the new international center alone, but perhaps the Ford Foundation, the Rockefeller Foundation and the Mexican government working together can get it established."

Thus did the Mexican president lob a bombshell that would, in

CAREER SAVER #33

Fate's thirty-third facilitator, Adolfo López Mateos, president of Mexico. President Lopez Mateos was supposed to close out the Rockefeller Foundation program in his country, but had recently visited Asia and had received accolades for the advances his country had achieved with wheat. He heard and saw how methods pioneered in Mexico were at the heart of a powerful and creative movement in world agriculture. Thus, instead of closing the program, he urged that the work in Mexico should be expanded, and he wanted to encourage the formation of a new organization whose work would have a greater international character. Thus was born the International Center for Maize and Wheat Improvement, which would provide Borlaug a career bringing wheat to the world.

time, provide Borlaug a proper workplace and the world a proud new hunger-fighting command.

Legal documents formalizing the Mexican president's casual suggestion were signed on October 25. At least on paper there now existed the International Corn and Wheat Improvement Center (known as CIMMYT from its Spanish acronym).

Wellhausen was designated Director General and director of the corn activities. Borlaug would direct the wheat activities, but by mutual consent was kept out of the administration chain of command.

For this nonprofit international organization that would project Mexico's knowledge to the wider world the future looked bright. Though many tortuous issues needed resolving before structures could be built and major programs begun, Borlaug was back in the fold. No longer need he report to the Mexican government. His boss once again was George Harrar in New York City. Apart from that he could be his own man all over again.

That November Indian and Pakistani scientists sowed the half-ton seed lots Pan Am had flown in from Mexico. Borlaug's gifts were used to establish plots on experiment stations and in farmers' fields scattered throughout both their wheatlands.

Shortly thereafter, Haldore Hanson invited Norm back to inspect Pakistan's plantings. Having considered he'd already done his part and certain that two visits within the same year was wildly excessive, Norm went only reluctantly.

But events would vindicate Hanson's wile and wisdom. He had by then met most of the agricultural officials who needed to sign off on the adoption of Mexican wheats. Mobilizing his journalist's flair and skill, he'd compressed Borlaug's technical notions into brief, hard-hitting prose. Knowing he needed to impact the minds of officials who knew no science he pressed home Norm's ultimate conviction that Pakistan could double the national wheat harvest *in eight years*.

Now with the creator on hand and his 20-page report freshly typed, he contacted Malik Khuda Bakhsh. Intrigued, the genial agriculture secretary invited both Hanson and Norm to afternoon tea.

The two showed up at his home on the outskirts of Lahore expecting a quiet chat but instead found the large villa stuffed with officials from universities and government, experts from extension services, and administrators from several food-related agencies.

This was disconcerting:

We hadn't expected speaking to a professional audience and had to rapidly rearrange our presentations, making them much more precise and official sounding.

Hal opened the proceedings with a step-by-step exposition exposing the issues holding back Pakistan's wheat production. He did it brilliantly.

Then I explained how Mexico was being transformed, adding that during the previous years five young Pakistani scientists had been trained and could transform this country in exactly the same way. I told about Bajwa and Chaudry's results at Lyallpur that I'd seen back in March. And I explained what the four plots signified for Pakistan's future.

Finally I summed up by reiterating my belief that Pakistan could double its wheat production *in eight years*.

The audience heard out these foreign foundations' representatives in total silence, and the lack of applause or appreciation indicated that no minds had been changed. The room was redolent with rejection. Norm was dismayed:

Even as Hal and I were driven away we knew that opposition was breaking out.

Across the border, Swaminathan moved quickly after Ralph Cummings handed him Borlaug's report and trucked over the half ton of seed Pan Am had supplied from the skies.

Dividing the seed into 14 equal lots, Swaminathan distributed those to 14 agricultural institutions across the wheat-growing areas. As a result, *Sonora 64*, *Mayo 64* and *Lerma Rojo 64* got their first chance to shine in the front lines of the global hunger fight.

One of the tests was at Swaminathan's own institute, the IARI. Another was at the Punjab Agricultural University in Ludhiana. The 12 other tests were run at state agricultural institutions.

As Wheat Coordinator, Swaminathan laid out a formal set of research protocols. His written instructions made one point crystal clear: every institution had to follow the protocols. With the plants handled identically in the 14 locations, any differences in the results would reflect scientific realities and not the preferences of the individuals handling them.

Progress was on the way. Mexican wheats were getting their first scientific measurements on the planet's hungriest side. The procedures were following professional research protocols. Next April everyone would know just how Borlaug's leading Mexican wheats would perform in South Asia.

At the same time Swaminathan divided into three equal lots the small samples gathered from 225 of Borlaug's best performers. He distributed those to the IARI, the Punjab Agricultural University in Ludhiana, and the Uttat Pradesh Agricultural University in Pantnagar.

Those were just for purposes of inspection. They would be planted in 225 tiny plots – each one labeled with the Borlaug's coding number.

They of course included seed from some of Borlaug's still-developing 8156 dwarf generation. No one expected anything to develop from them. They were, after all, his discards.

5
1964
Plants

IN MEXICO THE FIFTH YEAR opens with the promise of a great leap forward. Borlaug's latest and potentially greatest wheat generation is being bulked up in preparation for its grand opening on the food stage.

Getting this far has involved a long journey. Since discovering eight forgotten seeds in an old envelope in 1956, he's devoted 17 seasons and 8156 separate cross-pollinations to perfecting this half-height food producer. The successful survivors are still unnamed but their day of debut has been penciled in on the social calendar.

These four represent a major break from the past. They are super efficient – partitioning more growth into grain than into leaf and stem. They don't bend before the breeze. They're immune to the most devastating strains of the most devastating diseases. They mature in four months rather than five. They're at home in wheatlands from Canada to Argentina. They sprout four, five or even six separate stems, each hefting its own head of grain. Their small footprint allows farmers to cram several into the space previously occupied by one plant. Each of their heads bears about twice the normal number of grains. And those grains are great breadmakers.

These All-Stars satisfy the trifecta of constituencies he'd always hoped to serve. They are a farmer's fantasy, a miller's delight and a baker's dream. Soon the world will determine whether they're also a consumer's comfort.

In February 1964 Pakistan's National Action Planning Committee invited Norm to return and formally present the case for Mexican wheat. Comprising agricultural leaders from government and universities, this group had been tasked with plotting Pakistan's path forward on the food front.

This was Norm's second trip in two months, and it proved a horror. Before his flight could get out of New York several feet of snow buried the runways. A taxi inched him through the frozen streets of Queens, but no rooms were left at any inn. So he returned to Kennedy International Airport – newly named by a nation shellshocked by the assassination just two months ago – and whiled the night away, sleepless on a bench.

Next day, he departed on Pan Am's famous Flight 002 that flew eastbound around the world. Despite a vexing inability to sleep on planes, he remained unworried because following the long passage to Pakistan he'd have 24 hours to rest up.

However when the Boeing 707 reached Karachi at 4 am, the Ford Foundation driver meeting him in the terminal passed over a note: "Go to KLM Halfway House," it said, "take a shower and be back at the airport at 7 for a flight at 7:30." Turns out, the meeting had been moved up a day; it would be later that very same morning. And it would be in Lahore, which was still 600 miles away!

On reaching the Department of Agriculture in Lahore he'd gone sleepless more than 48 hours. Thus it was mortifying to find a formidable assortment of dignitaries sitting silent, still and straight-backed around one side of a polished table in a formal chamber.

This unwelcoming committee included the deputy agriculture minister, three research-center directors, two university vice-chancellors, and senior wheat scientists from Pakistan's three main wheat-growing regions.

On Norm's side of the table were Hal Hanson; Oddvar Aresvik, a Norwegian economist Hanson had recently embedded in the agriculture ministry; and Nacho Narvaez, who happened to be passing through to check on the local Wheat Apostles — a procedure instigated following Norm's disillusionments at Lyallpur and Cairo the previous year.

From the opening words the four foreigners appreciated they were about to undergo professional prosecution. It was a trial whose transcript Norm never forgot:

> The vice-chancellor of the University of Sindh spoke first. He was a scientist of national distinction, but he began by waving Hal Hanson's report in the air and quoting my words then declaring: "Stop to think of what kind of foolishness this is."
>
> Coming in for special scorn was my claim that Pakistan could

farm country. Farmers were excited. Some seemed likely to get an unbelievable 3 tons an acre. Previous harvests had typically been less than half a ton and even 1 ton had seemed unreachable.

Here's where pessimism began to dissipate. Even a few formerly immutable critics caught the wave of enthusiasm. It was the surf before the storm.

Norm was amazed:

> During our tour in March of '67 we encountered farmers — both large and small — who were eager to be part of the new prosperity. I was reminded of the 1930s, when hybrid corn was first planted on the Borlaug farm.
> This grass-roots enthusiasm was beginning at just at the right moment because much of the Indian government was still reluctant to commit to the widespread adoption of the package of seed and technology. In this, Pakistan was two years ahead. In India, Mrs. Gandhi and minister Subramaniam were committed but government officials were still reluctant.

New Delhi's brassbound reluctance was exemplified by the approach to fertilizer production. The Planning Commission was at that moment half-heartedly negotiating construction of fertilizer factories by private companies. In Socialist India that was an anathema, and, possibly to ensure failure, the commission dictated ruinous requirements and ridiculously low rates of return. Then out of the blue it decreed that all companies must submit their bids by midnight March 31st or forgo participation in the industry.

This was foolish but Norm felt sure the government would never relent. National elections were being held, and for the first time since Independence the vote was not predictable. For two decades the Congress Party had swept the polls; now, however, the masses were hungry and restive, and this election might prove a shocker.

Norm, however, was too buoyed up to worry about politics:

> We had to report our findings to the Minister of Agriculture. I was looking forward to informing Subramaniam that everything he'd dreamed of was starting to come to pass.
> Then, on March 29th, as we prepared to leave Ludhiana, a telegram arrived from Subramaniam himself. It said that we were invited to have lunch at the Escort Tractor Factory in the city of Meerut; we could stop off while en route to New Delhi. Poland had funded the factory and the luncheon would honor the Polish ambassador.
> We arrived just before noon to find hundreds of farmers

gathered for something like an agricultural fair. In the factory's forecourt small tractors stood in long gleaming lines. It sure looked impressive but one of my colleagues explained that there were two tractor companies and both were having difficulty selling their products; the accumulation of unsold inventory was causing concern. This day, the farmers didn't seem to be showing much interest either.

Presently we retired to a large and crowded room for the luncheon. I was placed near the president of the Escort Tractor Company, Mr. Nanda. A large number of journalists were on hand, as is common whenever a member of the diplomatic corps speaks.

Following the lunch Mr. Nanda rose and introduced the ambassador, who talked at length about the role of agricultural machinery in communist Poland.

Before closing the proceedings, Mr. Nanda introduced me and asked if I'd say a few words. Grabbing the microphone I described the outstanding success we'd seen everywhere during the past three weeks. I spoke of the enthusiasm of the farmers for the new wheats and the package of production technologies.

I closed with a special message to the journalists: "The grass roots are afire," I said, "and if the Government of India stimulates the adoption of this new technology, it will trigger a revolution in wheat production."

I indicated that government should provide the farmers:

- The right kind of fertilizer at reasonable prices;
- Credit for purchasing fertilizer and seed; And
- A fair price for the harvest.

That price, I said, should be roughly the international market price, or twice the present amount.

Then, for the journalists' benefit, Norm appended a summary:

During the last two weeks I've seen the beginnings of a wheat revolution in your fields.

If the government gives full support, India can replace famine with plenty.

What India needs now is fertilizer, fertilizer, fertilizer; credit, credit, credit; and fair prices, fair prices, fair prices!

Those will give India more food.

If I were a member of your parliament, I would leap from my seat every 15 minutes and shout, "Fertilizers!"

No matter what the subject of debate, I would shout, "Fertilizers! Give the farmers fertilizers!"

This being Election Day he finished up by warning what would happen if these things were not done:

> Unless there is more food, a volcano will erupt under this land's political leaders. The people will throw them out of office.

Around that vast and people-choked room a roar of laughter rose. Everybody seemed to be chuckling. The press loved it; Norm could see them scribbling as the applause rolled on and on.

But from the officials at the head table there emanated silence. This bumptious American had hijacked their meeting's purpose.

Actually, Norm tended to sympathize. For years to come, his ill-manners bothered his mind. He'd not been attentive. He'd gone too far. He'd not said the right things:

> As I took my seat I noticed that the Polish ambassador seemed upset. It was only then that I realized that I hadn't even mentioned the importance of his government's tractors.

The next day they arrived in the capital to find New Delhi in ferment. The Congress Party had suffered a shocking setback. Panicked over the famine and the uncertain food situation, Indians had voted out of office a third of the party's incumbents. The political elite whose domination had been almost unchallenged since India's founding, had suffered a deep wound.

Swaminathan and Norm went immediately to see the agriculture minister. Norm was bubbling:

> I made a dramatic entrance, pointing toward the window and asked Subramaniam: "Do you know what is going on out there? A revolution is starting. You must take action. Farmers are demanding more support. You must double and treble everything — fertilizer, water, credit."

Subramaniam held up a fistful of newspaper clippings from the morning papers and shouted: "Dr. Borlaug, you don't have to persuade me. I know what you said yesterday. I know what you are up to and I agree with you. But it is already too late for me. I've lost my seat in the Lok Sabha. As of tomorrow night, I'm out of office, so I cannot help any more!"

That news was so devastating Norm never got over it:

> We'd lost our leader. He'd focused so much on solving the food problem he hadn't gone home to campaign. It was not only tragic but ironic. Food shortages had terrified the voters. He'd done more than anyone to avert those shortages; he'd been the

backbone that gave the effort strength. And he'd been too conscientious to tend to his career.

Now there'd be a new minister of food and agriculture, and I feared the newcomer would bow before the critics' blandishments.

Then suddenly the minister seemed distracted by a new thought: "Before you leave," he barked, "please go see Ashok Mehta. He is chairman of the Commission whose plans you are always criticizing. He is also in charge of fertilizer imports and fertilizer industry development."

Then came another thought: "How long will you be in Delhi?"

"I leave for Mexico tomorrow night at midnight."

With that, Subramaniam grabbed the phone on his desk and arranged for Borlaug and Swaminathan to meet the Deputy Prime Minister the following evening at six.

As we left the minister's office I felt depressed and sad. Then he came to the door and yelled down the corridor: "Dr. Borlaug, speak bluntly. Hit him hard, just as hard as you hit me. He needs to hear it straight from the shoulder!"

On the evening of the 31st of March, just as we were about to enter the Deputy Prime Minister's office, I said to Swaminathan, "I'm going to follow Subramaniam's suggestion. This meeting will likely be stormy, so you'd better keep a low profile. I could be banned from returning to India and, should that happen, you and Glenn will have to keep the program moving forward."

Ashok Mehta met us with polite greetings, and I explained what was happening in the wheat fields. I emphasized that untold thousands of farmers, small and large, had seen how the new wheat could increase production. "The grass roots are on fire" I said, "and you can expect an explosion because all those small farmers plan to plant Mexican wheats in November."

Their expectations, I stressed, could never become realities until the government discarded its current policies. Those, I said, were now obsolete. A new bold approach is needed. In particular the government must greatly expand the availability of fertilizer.

Ashok Mehta interjected to say that India did not have the foreign exchange to boost fertilizer imports, much less build large fertilizer factories.

I countered by saying that the development of a fertilizer industry was more important than any other sector, since fertilizer was essential for keeping crops fed and that was essential for keeping the populace fed.

"Ours is a socialistic government," he explained, "We cannot let companies build fertilizer plants."

"Mr. Deputy Prime Minister," I said, "in Mexico there is a socialistic government, and it allows companies to build fertilizer plants."

Then I raised the financial issues.

"You must greatly expand credit for farmers, so they can buy fertilizer and the best seed. Also you must discard the cheap food policy that subsidizes city folk at the farmer's expense. You must assure the farmers they'll get a fair price for their grain. You should double the payment to match the market price in the rest of the world.

Then I issued a blunt warning: "Unless the policy is changed soon, farmers will riot and social and political disorder will spread across the countryside. If this happens, you Mr. Minister will be ousted. Moreover, the Congress Party will go down to defeat and you personally will be to blame!"

My voice was rising. In all of India I was probably the only man who could have shouted down the deputy leader in his own office. Perhaps understandably, he reacted indignantly. For several minutes there was chaos with both of us yelling at each other until we both ran out of breath.

Finally, I brought the confrontation to a close. "Mr. Minister," I said, "I leave soon on a flight to Mexico. I must say these things that you do not like."

Leaning across the desk and looking into his astonished eyes, I commanded, "Tear up those five-year plans. Start again and multiply everything for farm support three or four times. Increase your fertilizer, increase your support prices, increase your loan funds. Then you will be closer to what is needed to keep India from starving.

"IMAGINE YOUR COUNTRY FREE OF FAMINE," I shouted. "IT IS WITHIN YOUR GRASP!"

Ten days later, following his return to Sonora, Norm received a series of clippings from India's major newspapers, which the Rockefeller Foundation and Ford Foundation offices in New Delhi had forwarded. Dated April 1, 1967 they disclosed momentous news: "Last night at midnight the policies of the Government of India were changed." Ashok Mehta, they explained, was reopening negotiations with foreign chemical companies. The former decree that would have voided all uncompleted contracts for construction or financing of fertilizer factories was itself voided. Companies now had to at least the end of the year, and perhaps beyond, to submit their contracts.

This was revolutionary. India was downgrading its monocular focus on industrialization and lifting its sights to food production.

"The best hour of Dr. Borlaug's life," Subramaniam later reflected, "was that hour he spent with Ashok Mehta."

When the April harvest tallies were in, it became apparent that India's wheat production had soared to 16 million tons. The previous year it had been 11 million tons.

By now Pantnagar University had 7000 acres under wheat and had bought five combines to harvest it. A researcher recalls how "an auditor demanded to know why we were growing wheat where formerly we were growing sugarcane. But soon thereafter the reason was plain. The farm that before averaged not more than a million rupees net profit was providing a profit of 15 million rupees! The farm ended up supporting the University, and did so for seven more years."

Norm had only just arrived in Sonora when telegrams from Pakistan began urging that he "get the Mexipak seed." This is when Norm learned that Malik Khuda Bakhsh had not after all given up his ridiculous notion.
Against his better judgment he visited Yaqui Vargas. Nothing he said could pry any loose.

> Finally I was informed that Pakistan was sending its agriculture minister to buy *40,000 tons* of seed. There was but one catch: he'd buy nothing until he first got *2000 tons* of Mexipak White.
> I couldn't believe it. Yaqui Vargas was the only source of Siete Cerros, and he probably didn't have 2000 tons. Even if he did, he'd *never* sell his whole stash.

That May, shortly after the Sonora harvest had been completed, a passel of Pakistani officials arrived in Obregón City. It was led by the country's highest agriculture official, a Bengali from East Pakistan where only rice grew. Upon arrival he announced he'd come to buy 40,000 tons of seed wheat but absolutely, positively would not buy a single kernel until he had 2000 tons of the white-seeded version. Without that, he said, *he would buy nothing at all*.

This put Norm in a quandary: he immediately advised the farmers' co-ops in the area around the Sonora's state capital of Hermosillo, the five nearby Yaqui Valley farmer co-ops, various credit unions, the independent farmers association and the government organization representing poor farmers, the *ejiditarios*. The meeting was set for two o'clock the following afternoon at the Costa de Oro.

Norm went along to introduce the visitors:

The motel's small meeting room was packed with representatives from every farmer organization. Mexico's agriculture
minister had sent Roberto Osoyo, to chair the session. The
Pakistanis were there. Yaqui Vargas was there, seemingly
somewhat unsteady. And I was there.

Speaking in Spanish, Sr. Osoyo welcomed everyone and
explained the meeting's purpose was to bargain over the export
of this extraordinary amount of wheat seed. Then he turned the
microphone over to me. I introduced Pakistan's minister of
agriculture and explained the background to his request,
emphasizing how the new seed could offset his country's famine.

Then I proceeded to leave the room. The bargaining was
something wholly between the Mexicans and Pakistanis and I
neither needed nor wanted to be present. But as I stood up the
Pakistani minister leaned over and grabbed my arm. "No, no," he
said. "You are now my personal representative. I don't
understand Spanish, and I want to know what I'm dealing with
here. SIT DOWN!"

This arrangement was explained to the audience. Then the
bargaining began. There was only one question to start with:
Who would provide the 2000 tons of Siete Cerros? And of course
there was only possible source, who'd made clear he wasn't going
to give any up.

But soon everyone in the room was glaring at him, and after a
while the tension started wearing him down. Grudgingly, he
offered 200 kilos (500lb). It was pitiful. The glaring went on. The
bargaining went on too. Rising by 200 kilo increments until, about
an hour later, he'd conceded to sell a ton of Siete Cerros seed.

This was getting us nowhere. Pakistan's demand for 2000 tons
seemed so far off that the other farmers were getting angry.

To me, Vargas' personal position was clear too: He was on the
horns of a personal dilemma. If he grew his seed one more
season, he could make a fortune selling it to farmers.

But the others didn't understand, and didn't care. It was
agonizing to be in that room and feel the raw emotion flowing
from all sides. Amid the Mexican agony the Pakistanis remained
adamant. It was terrible. I could see the leaders of the credit
unions, good business people, nearly frothing at the mouth in
frustration. To them the golden prize of selling 40,000 tons of
seed was being held hostage by one of their own number.

Finally, Yaqui Vargas got to 1500 tons. That was as far as
anyone could push him. Probably it was all he had. I guess he
decided that selling it was probably better than being forever
ostracized. Mexicans were less individualistic than Americans;
public opprobrium more powerful.

Then the Pakistanis agreed to regard 1500 tons as satisfactory.
In less than five minutes they bought the other 40,000 tons.
Contracts amounting to millions of dollars were agreed to in

seconds. Most were for Super X, which had originally come from Yaqui Vargas too.

In this painful manner the Pakistan delegation succeeded in buying 1500 tons of Siete Cerros (Mexipak White to them), 40,000 tons of Super X (Mexipak Red), 200 tons of Sonora 64, and 20 tons of the very latest improvement: INIA 66, the first summer wheat capable of producing 7000 lb – 3.5 tons – per acre.

In August 1967, the giant cargo was loaded at the port of Guaymas. Last year's 14,000 ton world record had now been crushed. This one was almost three times larger and filled *four ships*.

> I drove the 80 miles from Ciudad Obregón, and what a thrill it was to see those lined up along the dock, each being loaded with grain. This hive of activity made me think back to the moribund state of production in 1944 when local millers had shunned their own farmers and bought wheat in Canada and the U.S. These days, the world clamored for Mexican wheat.

Despite this being a Pakistani initiative, critics around the world damned Borlaug for "forcing" this unprecedented transfer of wheat seed upon an innocent Asian nation. The implication was that he'd made a fortune on the backs of poor people. He, of course, made not one cent and had not instigated the operation. He'd actually attempted to head it off.

Norm was amazed at how such falsehoods could make headlines the world around:

> In the United States and Europe a number of prominent academics insisted I was guilty of gross irresponsibility. I was, they proclaimed, "playing with the lives of millions of innocent people." They implied that I just didn't know what I was doing.
>
> Despite their distant viewpoint and lack of first-hand facts, they knew that sending wheat seeds halfway around the world was a despicable act, aimed at duping the innocent peasant farmers of Asia who didn't know any better. My motivation, they implied, was either boosting my own ego or lining my own pocket.
>
> The pressure for the seed was of course coming from the Pakistanis themselves – none more so than those innocent naïve farmers, who right now just couldn't get enough of the Mexipaks.
>
> After the 40,000 tons of seed arrived, Pakistan's government sold it at an official price of 35 rupees a maund (about $200 a ton). But even at this steep rate there was insufficient to meet the demand. Seed began selling on the black market at prices up to three times higher.

That November, Pakistan planted Borlaug wheat on nearly 5 million acres, of those 3 million acres were sown to Mexipak Red. It's amazing to think that none of this would have happened without Yaqui Vargas. Mexican scientists were still striving for perfection and keeping the curvy sisters from formal release. Vargas' seed may have been of uncertain provenance but it was poised to prevent famine.

Having ditched all other options Pakistan had become utterly reliant on seed from the previous harvest, on the Mexipak seed from Staley Pitts, and on the seed from the four newly unladen ships. With all that Borlaug-bred seed the country launched itself into a new and unknown future.

Narvaez estimated that the new varieties sown that November were, in order of importance, Mexipak Red, Penjamo, Lerma Rojo, Mexipak White and Sonora 64.

During these days Ayub Khan and Nacho developed a surprising rapport. In his memoirs, Hanson provides an example:

"President Ayub Khan called Narvaez to Flagstaff House, the president's residence at Rawalpindi and asked for the results. Narvaez gave him the names of the landowners who achieved exceptional production, many of whom were the president's friends. The average yield from the Mexipaks was 2.5 and 3.0 tons, compared to Pakistan's old national average of 0.4 tons – the national standard between 1914 and 1964 that the Sindh professor had said would never change.

When Narvaez mentioned some failures, the president demanded names. Narvaez shuffled his feet, but the president insisted. Well, the young Mexican said, those men are well known to you.

The first was the secretary of agriculture [Malik Khuda Bakhsh].

Why?

Because, sir, he failed to instruct his farm manager about the new cultivation methods.

The president shook his head slowly. And the second failure?

That was the governor of West Pakistan [the Nawab of Kala Bagh]. Same reason.

And the third?

Narvaez looked steadily at the floor, then pointing a finger hesitantly at the president, he said: "The third, sir, was you. Same reason."

The president grimaced.

Although Pakistan's food problem was huge, it was of course dwarfed by the one across the border. India's situation seemed beyond solution. Hunger was so widespread in 1965 and 1966 it raised the specter of a starvation pervasive enough to have global effects. International observers concluded the imminence of a forced reduction of India's giant population – 397 million at decade's beginning, it had by 1967 reached 511 million. Millions of Indian boat people would soon flood the world in search of succor. It would be a humanitarian disaster of proportions seldom seen outside wartime.

Now everything was up to the scientists, and they were getting a grip on the situation at the grass roots. Anderson and Swaminathan co-opted the IARI and two of the new agricultural universities to multiply the seed.

Uttar Pradesh Agricultural University planted 11,000 acres, most of it to a local selection from what Norm called Line S308. Because of susceptibility to Mexican leaf-rust races, he'd rejected it. This was one of the 225 Pan Am had flown in in '63.

This Borlaug discard grew so well that the university offered discounted seed to any farmer who'd attend its field days. It set the price at 5 rupees a kilogram (about 30 cents a pound), and found itself besieged. Farmers not only came alone, they brought truckloads of friends, each of whom picked up his kilogram. Some promptly sold their stash for 25 rupees a kilo.

This experience was typical of many across northern India's irrigated wheat belt. Demand was insatiable. Faculty members — including the Vice Chancellor Dhyan Pal Singh, himself — plowed up the lawns in the backyards of their bungalows and grew wheat. Some students were allotted five-acre plots to raise the new wheats and make their tuition money. Faculty members planted the areas around their campus bungalows.

Norm was impressed:

> The fact that they went in for seed multiplication with such enthusiasm and shared the seeds they produced with relatives and friends for further multiplication was a key factor in spreading the new high yielding varieties.
>
> During the craze, many people took advantage of the easy money to be made. But as with anything of value, crime soon showed its ugly head. As harvest time approached, incidents began:
>
> The Indian Agricultural Research Institute had to post rifle-toting guards at its plots. Even so, one morning a guard was found tied to a tree, naked. He'd been stripped of his clothes; the

GUARDING THE SEED

Indian Agricultural Research Institute, New Delhi. So many farmers wanted Mexican wheats that guards had to be posted over the research plots like this one. After a robber held a knife at the watchman's throat while his confederate carried off the seed stock, some guards were armed. The black market price got so high that common criminals turned to seed snatching.

plot had been stripped of its seed.

Another of the IARI staff, a scientist named Tandon, who'd been posted to Lahaul, a beautiful valley on the way to Tibet, was travelling with a dozen mule loads of wheat seeds along the Rohtang Pass when bandits relieved him of the entire load!

During one night at the Punjab Agricultural University a band of farmers overpowered a guard and while some of them held a knife at his throat the others robbed the plots of all their seeds. (As it happened, they took some of the more infertile strains, so some unwitting farmer eventually suffered.)

It was common for experiment stations to find scarcely any wheat heads within arm's length of the paths through the plots. Visiting farmers had grabbed handfuls to hide in their voluminous pockets.

In light of the fact that we'd soon be deluged with criticism for "favoring only the rich farmers and neglecting the poor," it is worth noting that farmers of all levels of sophistication and wealth came desperately seeking the seed. And to even the poorest, cost never seemed an issue. Everyone wanted the new varieties; everyone somehow found the rupees.

Norm was happy to see all this ferment of activity, good and not so good. A stolen seed doesn't know it, and as he declared many times:

Wheat is an equal opportunity performer. It never discriminates. It grows as well for the poor as for anyone.

India now had on hand enough seed to sow close to 7 million acres — almost a ten-fold gain in area planted to Mexican dwarfs in one year. From that point on, it could sow all its irrigated wheatlands.

The intensive breeding work culminated, in 1967, in the release of six Indian variants of dwarf wheat. All were white-seeded and highly rust-resistant.

As the November sowing season approached, the government had to choose which variety to multiply for release to farmers. In 1967 the two names were combined to form "Kalyansona."

Line S308 was bred in Mexico, but because it was susceptible to Mexican races of leaf rust, it was never released to Mexican farmers. After seed samples arrived, Indian scientists made selections for resistance to stem rust and leaf rust, and from this process, Sonalika emerged. This was released in India in 1967 under the name Sonalika. Later, Pakistani farmers obtained seed from Indians along their common border, and in Pakistan it was designated Blue Silver.

In Pakistan during this time when farmers and politicians were turning into avid supporters, foreign experts remained doubters. Such experts were then legion in Pakistan. The World Bank, for instance, had three foreign consulting firms studying the country's agriculture and water supply.

I was never too impressed. These "experts" may have been good at assessing the agriculture of the present, but they were hopeless at envisioning any future other than a straight-line continuation of what they'd documented. Any change in course threw them for a loop.

One major thing they routinely overlooked was a change in the spirit of the farmers, scientists and government officials. That was unquantifiable but vitally important. Far from being disembodied and divorced from emotion, economic development has a human dynamic. Indeed, the locals' own enthusiasm, determination and optimism is more important than almost anything else. Its lack accounts for the many failures in foreign assistance programs.

One day, two of the World Bank consultants came to our test plots in Lyallpur. I spent two hours with them, patiently explaining what the Mexican plants meant for Pakistan's future. I showed how a big leap in productivity was imminent. But the economists, who were both Dutch, just smiled indulgently and dismissed both me and any possible course change for the country's agriculture. I'm sure they thought I was some sort of starry-eyed dreamer. Maybe that's understandable, considering that the sights elsewhere around Pakistan seemed to belie everything I was saying.

Aresvik later related his view of this incident: "I remember one day when we were visiting Ayub Agricultural Research Institute at Lyallpur, two agricultural experts from a Dutch consulting firm happened to be there. It was easy to see that they did not believe [Borlaug] and simply laughed at his ideas."

Norm found it no laughing matter:

This was tremendously frustrating and even discouraging. We were winning over the Pakistanis from the top of the government to the most impoverished farmer, but we couldn't budge the Western authorities. For two years I worked to convince the World Bank's foreign consulting firms that change was coming and the farmers would adopt it enthusiastically. I failed miserably, and in 1966 the consultants submitted a voluminous investigation proclaiming a dismal prospect for Pakistan's wheat production.

When it was eventually published this so-called "Comprehensive Report" took up 23 hefty and expensively printed volumes. Three were devoted to agriculture, and the sum and substance of their advice to Pakistan was: invest as little as possible in agriculture . . . put in moneys sufficient only to maintain the country's political stability. In other words, invest just enough to avoid rural riots. This was necessary, the report proclaimed, because there can be no improvement in Pakistan's farm output until 1985 at the earliest.

The authors had everything carefully documented. They'd worked everything out with graphs and tables to show the authenticity of their conclusions. They projected that the dwarf wheats would occupy 50 percent of the land by 1985, which was almost 20 years into the future. They also claimed that Pakistan's wheat yields might possibly double, but not before the end of the 20th century — 34 years hence. In light of this they were especially opposed to investments in full-sized fertilizer factories, which would obviously be a waste of money. Instead, those Western advisors claimed that a single half-sized factory was all the country needed.

These people were talking in decades. Their kind of pessimism was likely to turn off both World Bank loans and foreign investments, which would bring about exactly the result they predicted.

Fortunately, the president and the agriculture minister were more realistic than their high-paid advisors and 23 very expensive volumes of advice. Hailing from a farm background and still a practicing farmer on the side, Ayub understood the explosive potential of combining dwarf wheat, fertilizer and irrigation. He'd seen it in his own garden. Also, the president was convinced that fertilizer factories would pay for themselves in a few short years. By that narrow margin was the program saved from a policy that would have let millions starve in the years just ahead.

However, the World Bank report was damaging nonetheless: The Esso Pakistan Fertilizer Company built the half-sized factory that the experts said was all the country needed. But before its completion fertilizer usage had jumped almost threefold, something the foreign advisors hadn't conceived remotely possible *ever*. Had enough capacity been built from the start, fertilizer would have been a lot cheaper.

In India by March 1967 the 18,000 tons of imported Mexican wheat seed – sown the previous November – was reaching maturity on over 700,000 acres. This brought on a great new controversy regarding the best strategy for fertilizing the plants.

Given India's worn-out soils, fertilizer would be a critical constituent in the operations for growing enough grain to feed the hungry. If Mexican seed was the catalyst for greater food production, fertilizer was the fuel feeding the engine that would feed the multitudes.

Yet fertilizer use was vigorously opposed. Most vehement of all in this struggle were the academic and agricultural economists who marshaled "irrefutable" reasons why little or no fertilizer should be used.

This was utter folly, given the hunger breaking out all round, and we ignored it. However, even within our own ranks a battle of wills arose because the country didn't have enough fertilizer for every farmer to employ the ideal amount. The immediate issue, therefore, was whether some farmers should get the ideal amount or whether all farmers should get some share.

Glenn Anderson and I were for the first idea, and insisted that the maximum recommended amount — 120 lb of nitrogen and 40 lb of phosphorus per acre — be provided to farmers until the supplies were gone.

On the other side was everyone else: the economists from the Ministry of Agriculture, the Planning Commission, and even most of my Rockefeller Foundation colleagues. They all insisted that the fertilizer recommendations should be scaled back to 40 pounds of nitrogen and 20 pounds of phosphorus per acre. That way, they said, three times more area and three times more families could benefit.

At first sight, their view seemed logical and most equitable. But Glenn and I argued that this was the wrong moment because everyone would get only modest yield improvements — maybe rising from 800 to 1000 lb an acre. But with the whole program teetering on the verge of takeoff we needed a demonstration dramatic enough to sweep away all reluctance and resistance.

The strategic dilemma we were wrestling with had more to do with psychology than science. We knew from Mexico that traditional farmers readily accept practices that double or triple yield but reject practices that increase production only 10 or 20 percent.

"I want the differences in yield to be so big that everything the farmers have believed in comes down in shambles all around them," I said. "The object is to produce 5000 to 6000 lb an acre or even more, and thereby create cultural shock. When the peasant farmer gets five or six times the income the new methods and practices will be adopted and the resistance and argumentation will disappear."

At one point, the debate became over emotional. Only with Ralph Cummings' quiet, measured diplomacy were we finally all calmed down. Glenn and I nonetheless stood our ground and eventually we prevailed. The higher fertilizer rate was applied, and fewer farmers got the benefit.

At that point everyone sat back to see if that call had been right.

By now Swaminathan, Anderson and a growing team of cooperators are building strong technical supports.

The researchers were concerned that disease could break out. For the rust-resistance research thousands of individual plants were inoculated, one at a time, by hand syringe with all the known rust races. Only the survivors were carried forward in the breeding work.

> This was a safety precaution. Too many lives were at stake to take any chances with a rust epidemic.
>
> Previously, it was only at IARI that breeders and pathologists were working together; but with the new varieties and the diseases that affected them, they began to do so at many other centers as well. So with these new varieties, many centers began taking pathology more seriously.

Across India's wheat country there was now a rush toward descendants from Borlaug's Cross 8156. For the moment the white Siete Cerros and the red Super X are transcendent, but the local improved versions are coming on line and showing their strengths.

Norm was always amazed at all the good his hastily contributed seed that came from embarrassingly bad plants had produced:

> Three leading Indian varieties came from that shipment from Mexico in 1963 — but each of them narrowly escaped oblivion. I'd included them in the collection sent out for rust testing, but later we threw the remaining stocks away because the plants proved unsatisfactory in Mexico.
>
> It was the Indian plant breeders and Glenn Anderson who recognized this material as special, and today all three varieties made major contributions not only in that country but throughout southern Asia.
>
> Kalyan Sona was a wonderful variety. It resisted the major diseases prevalent in India: black rust, yellow rust, brown rust and loose smut. And it was so adaptable it could be grown in the cool of Kashmir and in the tropical heat of Coimbatore in the southern hills. It matured quickly and yielded well.

Glenn Anderson was the godfather of all this in the sense that he supported it with Rockefeller Foundation funds and guided it with his collegial presence and his understanding of the wheat plant. He kept the whole focus forever on practical progress. Together with Swaminathan, who led the technical teams, they made an unbeatable combination.

1968
Production

HE NINTH YEAR BEGINS with the Western world atwitter. The 20th Century's midlife crisis is now exposed for all to see. Food production is maxed out, humans are at carrying capacity, 3 billion more are headed earthward, and the first arrivals are already beginning to find the pantry bare.

This year brings Paul Ehrlich's bestselling *The Population Bomb*, whose pages declare: "The battle to feed humanity is over. In the 1970s, the world will undergo famine — hundreds of millions of people are going to starve to death in spite of any crash program embarked upon now."

This Stanford University insect specialist and other equally apt experts on global food production dished out such unrelenting doses of a nerve-shattering negativity that the inevitability of global famine became accepted fact. None sought out Borlaug, none included his views, none referenced his work. None cared to know an alternate future might be pending; it spoiled the story line.

Likely, that neglect made no difference. Thanks to the newly discovered magic of the media, Westerners disbelieved good news. The Vietnam War, the Cold War's threat of nuclear annihilation, President Kennedy's assassination, the rise of breast-beating environmentalism, and the battle for civil rights predisposed the American mind to believe that the future would be bad. It was an apocalyptic time and the fact that impoverished nations were poised on the brink of a food shortfall big enough to plunge millions into an abyss of misery and death was wholly consistent with the media narrative embedded in the Western consciousness. The title of a popular 1960s musical summed up the feeling: "Stop the World, I Want to Get Off."

Even highly respected thinkers predicted that mass starvation would in the mid-1970s sweep the globe like a human scythe. C.P. Snow, the great British philosopher and physicist prophesied that within ten years: "many millions of people in the poor countries are going to starve to death before our eyes . . . we shall see them doing so upon our television sets."

Borlaug, however, knew better. Descendants of his 8156th dwarf-wheat cross are spreading faster than any crop variety in history. That very year those high-yield food suppliers are being planted on 6.7 million acres in India, 1.8 million acres in Pakistan, 1.3 million acres in Mexico, 420,000 acres in Turkey, 65,000 acres in Afghanistan, 61,000 acres in Nepal. And that's just the beginning. Acreage is starting to increase in Argentina, Brazil, Chile, U.S., Canada, South Africa, Morocco, Tunisia, Australia and more. Their secret: dwarf wheats do more than lift food output; they lift family income.

On his sixth March Mission he found South Asia undergoing transformation. Throughout the Ganges and Indus basins the food rush had begun. Thanks to the 40,000 ton Mexican wheat-seed importation, Pakistan has enough to plant 3 million acres. More than 30,000 demonstration plots, contrasting the old and the new, had been placed across the region.

Like the hybrid corn of his own youth, high-yield wheat was an agent of basic change. It was a prosperity transformation, lifting poverty as it lifted hunger. And it was a peaceful transformation.

Still and all, many obstructionists refuse to concede. Once more they raised the seed-color canard. As in Pakistan a commonsensical administrator overrode the fear-mongers. Swaminathan credits Anthony Lancelot Dias, who was then the Food Secretary to the Government of India. "He sought my views on the policy to be adopted during 1968. I explained the yield advantage of Lerma Rojo and requested that both red and amber grain varieties be given the same procurement price. Any price distinction influenced the farmer. Dias agreed, and without his decision we would not have had the same success. Even a 5 or 10 rupee difference would have lessened the spread of Lerma Rojo, the highest yielding variety and the main source of the high production during 1968 and 1969."

For years to come clueless diehards kept on claiming that Indians never ate red wheat even though most Indians, most Americans, and most of those critics were eating red wheat every day. Soon it was bandied around as a fundamental flaw behind Borlaug's efforts. The persons making that claim didn't know that the name referred to the color of the skin that was milled off long before any flour was made.

Yet this popular delusion swept on unrelenting. Journalists must have reported 10,000 times that Mexican wheats were all right in their way, but they were the wrong color.

Then arose a second purely cosmetic issue: seed size. Because the Mexican grains were a little smaller, India's grain merchants refused to pay farmers the full price. As far as food production was concerned, this was foolish. Seed size meant nothing. Per pound or per bushel, small and large grains produced the same amount of food. Norm was again livid that people were growing lesser-yielding plants merely because the grain was larger. But once again he could do nothing.

Early in March Swaminathan, Anderson, Kohli, and Borlaug retraced their journey of the previous spring. Most farmers had now switched to Mexican wheats. It was just a few weeks before the peak of the harvest, and from the scenes all around they could sense a tremendous change unfolding. The roof over food production was literally lifting skyward.

One reason was the previous year's decision to restrict fertilizer. Culture shock was in evidence. Fertilizer had turbo-charged the high powered plants to the top of their performance range, typically around 3 tons an acre. The farmers with fertilizer couldn't believe their luck; the rest couldn't believe their eyes, and were committed to catching up next season.

Part of their tour was in the irrigated districts of Punjab but part was farther east in the area where famine had raged just two years ago. Now it was a vast carpet of short, stiff-strawed, wheats, level as though freshly mowed, and hefting big heads loaded with plump grains. The magnificent 1967 monsoon had restored the soils in time for the November planting. Now the results were plain for all to see.

The last stage of the 12 hour drive from Ludhiana to Delhi was a ride through a region in flux. People seemed buoyed by hope. They were seizing the opportunity of their lives. The haunted hunger look, so recently apparent, was seldom seen. The countryside seemed somehow taller, lighter, brighter.

Even the unflappable scientist was moved:

> The transformation seemed nothing less than miraculous even to we who were mentally prepared. All of us felt a sense of privilege at being able to witness the Punjab that March. The weather had been good; the heads on the wheats were heavy.

AFTER BORLAUG . . .

Punjab State, 1968. Food was everywhere. It was said that "grain poured into rural towns in never-ending lines of bullock carts and trucks and on the backs of donkeys, mules and camels. Punjabi towns such as Ludhiana were literally wallowing in wheat." It was a gladening sight.

. . . FOOD WAS EVERYWHERE

People hereabouts mostly ground their own flour, and so were exposed to differences in seed size and seed color. Sadly, these workers seem to be sifting out the large grains to sell at a premium. Borlaug was forever railing against such practices because the large-seeded plants were often the lowest yielding.

We could see that the 1968 wheat harvest was going to be huge.

When we got back to Delhi we met with the newly installed agriculture minister and tried to convey something of what we'd seen. It was hard to get across the magnitude and significance of the forthcoming harvest and of the farmers' euphoria to someone who had no notion of what had gone before and, in fact, had not the vaguest idea of scientific agriculture. He was from the northeastern state of Assam, which grew no wheat.

In appearance, Jagjivan Ram was short and squat with a heavy frame and huge thick eyebrows. In manner, he was ponderous and pedantic and seemed a little lost. Now the whole plum of the food transformation fell right into his lap. He, not Subramaniam, got to reap the glory.

After seeing the new agriculture minister, Swaminathan and I went to pay our respects to Mrs. Gandhi. We had tea with her and I described the enthusiasm of the farmers using the new varieties and methods. I informed her of the bountiful harvest that was about to begin. Then I bluntly repeated my routine recommendation: "Madam Prime Minister, the grass roots are on fire over all this and unless fertilizer, credit and fair prices are forthcoming, there will be trouble. Hundreds of thousands of farmers now know what can be achieved, and if the government provides the support millions more will participate. Then India's food supply will soar. The game is won if you do these things."

Mrs. Gandhi made no particular comment, but asked a few thoughtful questions and I sensed she was putting the last of her doubts behind. Maybe even getting excited.

In New York that same April, the Rockefeller Foundation convened a symposium called Strategy for the Conquest of Hunger. Norm was asked to stop by on his way home from India. Crossing the Atlantic he happened to be on the same flight as Malik Khuda Bakhsh, and over lunch the agriculture minister confessed: "My dear doctor, I can now tell you some things. After you left that crucial meeting in 1964, most of the senior scientists were vehemently opposed to you. In the whole action planning group *not one member supported going ahead with the Mexican wheats*."

At the symposium the following day, Khuda Bakhsh announced to the world that the harvest then being gathered would make Pakistan self-sufficient in wheat production . . . two years before Borlaug's much-derided prediction. It no longer needed to import food grain from foreign countries.

For his part at that symposium Borlaug made a blunt comment:

The most conservative man in traditional agriculture is the

scientist, and sometimes I am not proud to be one of them. This is most discouraging. The scientist is a privileged person, the man who should lead us out of the wilderness of static, underproductive agriculture, and yet by his apathy and failure to exercise his unique vision, he keeps us in the swamp of despair.

The scientist fears change because he is in a relatively privileged position in his own society. If there is no breakthrough in yield, he will not be criticized. But if he makes a recommendation and something goes wrong, he may lose his job.

In many different countries there is no faith or understanding between the farmer and the scientist. Almost without exception the farmer says, "This man is a theorist. He is not a doer, and he can't help us." In the past; this complaint was all too often valid, but today the situation is rapidly changing.

Outside the capitals and confines of northern India and Pakistan not much of this was known. But the deluge of honors that would mark the rest of his days began this month.

In April he was elected a Member of the prestigious National Academy of Sciences. He was also honored by the American Agricultural Editor's Association and the National Council of Commercial Plant Breeders.

On May 17 Obregón City named a street in his honor. It was a wide boulevard that extended from the heart of the city miles out into the heart of the Yaqui Valley, now filled with square miles of his golden wheat. The tribute was popular: largely through his efforts the city, with its 170,000 people, was busy, prosperous and booming. By this time the farmers were annually providing the northeast agricultural research station, CIANO, with $400,000 – five times more than the Sonora and Mexican governments provided.

That August *World Farming* magazine featured a cover story devoted to his work [this book's cover features the photo used for that 1968 magazine cover].

Before the year was out a farsighted British television producer ATV had filmed a documentary on Norm and his work in Mexico. It called him the The Prophet of Wheat and made him its Man of the Year for 1968.

These were his first recognitions and he was nonplussed. He couldn't understand why people would want to honor someone who'd merely done his job.

In India when the harvest had been completed in May the world had changed.

Despite my normal optimism, I'd underestimated how big the harvest would be. The better farmers in the Punjab routinely achieved 3000 to 3500 lb an acre; some passed 5000. One was awarded a medal for attaining 7500 lb an acre.

I'd also underestimated the effects. Punjabi towns such as Ludhiana were literally buried in wheat. Town squares were filled with huge stacks of sacks.

Nothing like that had been seen before and in the barely controlled chaos that resulted, everything was lacking except food. For one thing, there was a shortage of labor. It seemed as if every person was busy, yet many more were needed. Farm families were working from before dawn till after dark cutting the plants with sickles and stacking the sheaves by hand, and still falling behind. No one had realized that it takes four times longer to cut and stack an acre of wheat when the yield is 5000 pounds than when it is 800 pounds.

No one had anticipated how much muscle power would be needed to haul all those heavy sheaves to the threshing floors. Nor had anyone prepared for the amount of time, effort, space and organization to thresh and winnow five times the normal amount. By tradition, threshing was accomplished by knocking the seeds off the cut stems by walking cows or buffalo over them. Winnowing involved tossing the resultant seeds into the air for the breeze to blow the husks away.

These methods could no longer cope. The harvest – which normally took three weeks – stretched beyond two months and became a major bottleneck. For one thing, there weren't enough threshing floors. For another, no one had foreseen what it would take to bag the threshed grain load it on trucks and railroad cars and move it out. There weren't enough bags to hold the grain, carts to haul the bags, bullocks to pull the carts, or trucks and trains to haul it away.

Worst of all, there were not enough storage warehouses. India had made no preparations for anything like this.

The culmination of the chaos came when the monsoon arrived in May 1968. It came three weeks early, and in many areas grain remained piled everywhere. Some was heaped up, unthreshed. Mountains of bagged grain stood by the railroad sidings, waiting for a train. When the monsoon rains began falling part of this was damaged or destroyed. In some areas local authorities closed the schools and packed sacks of grain into the classrooms. Kids could go outside, but not wheat.

When the dust had settled, the sweat had dried and the muscle-

SIGNAL HONOR

On May 17, 1968 the city of Obregón renamed one of its major thoroughfares "Calle Dr. Norman E Borlaug." The road stretches not only through the modern city but 30 miles out into the surrounding farming area. The honor had been pressed by the local Rotary Club, farmers' associations, and the municipality of Cajeme. The ceremony was held at the point where the avenue begins. The plaque unveiled that day states: "To the apostle of wheat and benefactor of agriculture in the Yaqui region with grateful recognition." The Avenue is the very same one that he'd been driven down when he first visited in 1945. Then it had been dusty dirt and had stretched out into the flats where the scenery resembled cactus-clad advertisements touting Arizona vacation. It now transits one of the world's greatest granaries.

aches faded, it became clear that 5 million *extra* tons of wheat had been added to India's national larder. This was a 60 percent increase over the two bad years of 1965 and 1966 and a 42 percent increase over 1964, the best wheat year India had ever enjoyed before Borlaug.

To all this, the farmers responded with excitement and impatience. According to calculations of the Indian Agricultural Research Institute, farmers who tried it made about three times more income per acre than their neighbors who stuck with the old varieties. They, too, were turning a mental corner, and no wonder: In some instances, yields were running seven times what they'd been just three years before.

India's wheat production rose to nearly 17 million tons in 1968, a leap of almost 30 percent. The new dwarfs had occupied 18 percent of the wheat area but produced 36 percent of the harvest. After several thousand years, the yield ceiling had been utterly smashed.

None of the Planning Commission's five-year plans had conceived so magnificent a makeover. Norm's greatest satisfaction was to see that Commission finally tear up its much-vaunted plans for heavy industries. Now it rushed to draw up plans for fertilizer imports, fertilizer factories, farmer credit, and for storing, transporting and marketing grain on a massive scale.

The Indian farmer and the Indian food supply at last had priority. And respect.

Only one thing remained bothersome:

> I felt terrible that Subramaniam had missed out on the satisfaction and recognition. "He'd been the architect of all that had transpired and in India the glory should have been his. He'd been proved right: His rash boast that not a single Indian would die of starvation had, in overall terms, been realized. So, too, had his claim that India would no longer import grain to keep its poor people from starvation.

Actually, Subramaniam's replacement proved better than Norm had anticipated. Early in 1968, when it became clear that India would be harvesting a record wheat crop, Jagjivan Ram requested Indira Gandhi to issue a special stamp to commemorate the "Wheat Revolution." He also suggested that the stamp should have the portrait of the library building of the Indian Agricultural Research Institute (IARI), in order to emphasize the role of science in transforming our agriculture.

In July, Indira Gandhi issued the postage stamp commemorating "India's Wheat Revolution 1968." It depicted three stylized heads of wheat and the library building of the Indian Agricultural Research Institute where in 1963 Norm had lunched with the dozen motivated visionaries and they had kicked everything off.

Although Mrs. Gandhi formally issued the stamp, she probably wished she'd heeded Norm's plea to build more godowns in rural towns. Indeed, one of the secondary fall-outs from the massive piles of grain stacked up everywhere was an overwhelming abundance of rats. A cartoonist for one of the New Delhi newspapers ran a caricature of the stamp over the label "India's Rat Revolution 1968."

Another thing for which there was no shortage was moneylenders.

With local markets flooded with grain, profiteers found opportunities to beat down the prices paid to farmers. Those middlemen could have reaped all the rewards, leaving the growers as poor as ever. However, the new agriculture minister began building storage warehouses and launched an aggressive procurement program. By paying about $2.75 a bushel he stabilized the market.

This was historic. The giant purchases gave the government a buffer stock big enough to protect India's giant population against future malign monsoons.

The government soon learned to use its stocks to dampen speculation. When consumer grain prices began to soar later in 1968, for example, it fed some of its buffer stock into the market to temper prices. The food supply was stabilized and for the first time under control.

By that time Norm was long back in Mexico training more youths from seemingly every country but India. His mind is lost in that task. And he's glad to be out of Asia's hoopla. Whenever he happens to reflect, his main thoughts are for the growers:

Of course the real unsung heroes were the millions of farmers who'd had the vision and courage to dump the methods that had been in use for 5000 years. It was they who supplied the grassroots fire that pressured the planners and political leaders into action. The "skinny, unskilled, tradition-bound" Indian farmer proved adventuresome, adaptable and even entrepreneurial when he could get five times more income from his labor. For me it was déjà vu all over again. As in the Iowa of my youth, a high-yielding crop had transformed the standard of living of subsistence farmers, and given them a life.

To have been part of that was satisfaction enough.

I n Pakistan the excitement was tempered by a decision Hanson's bosses in New York made. It would disgust Norm:

This was where we were about to leave a fingerprint on history. But while the crop was maturing the Ford Foundation pulled the rug out from under the whole endeavor. Someone in the New York headquarters — a person who clearly cared little for fighting famine or saving lives — decided that my colleague's tour of duty was over. The foundation refused to relent on its five-year limit. It offered Hanson a choice: Lagos, Rio de Janeiro, or resign.

Hal protested that in Nigeria or Brazil he'd have to start again and build up a whole new cadre of cooperators. But the New York

THE LEADER . . .

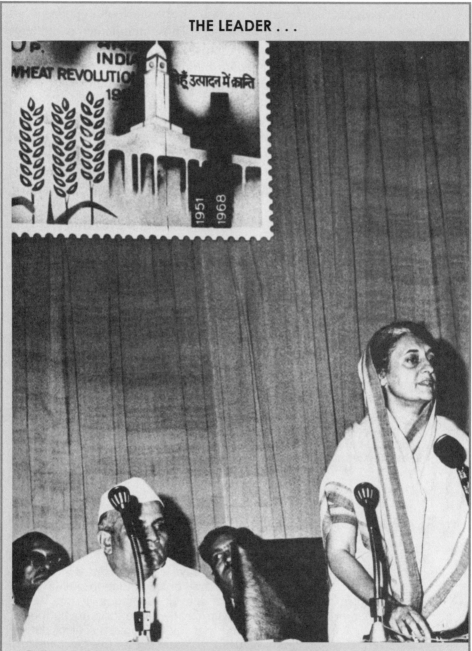

Indian Agricultural Research Institute, June 1968. Prime Minister Indira Gandhi had recently led her nation through its worst famine since independence was gained. But now with food production soaring she came to honor the place where just 5 years earlier Borlaug had lunched with a few Indian scientists . . . .

HONORS SCIENCE . . .

.... That meeting had catalyzed the revolution that led to this honor. Sadly former agriculture minister Subramaniam, who'd played the pivotal role at the policy level was not among those being honored. His replacement, Jagjivan Ram (glasses and white cap) got to enjoy the honors.

official would be swayed neither by logic nor a place in history. Employees could spend no more than five years in a country, regardless of whether the fate of millions might hinge on keeping the smooth-working operations in place a year or two longer.

Soon thereafter, Aresvik and Narvaez also were notified that they had to leave. Hanson was bundled off to Nigeria and Narvaez and Aresvik to Lebanon. None wanted to go. As hunger fighters none would ever rise to the same heights. And the countries they went to needed their talents far less than Pakistan.

Contemplating this situation still makes me furious. The Ford Foundation mindlessly disbanded what was arguably the greatest hunger fighting team, and did so based on a bureaucratic whim at a critical moment with uncertainty raging and lives on the line.

The incredible thing is that the Ford Foundation could have basked in a triumph. Its staff had achieved something close to a miracle. Hanson had guided the program magnificently. Aresvik sat right next to the minister, facilitating the rapid execution of policy decisions and timely release of financial support. And Nacho was collaborating with all Pakistan's wheat scientists and agricultural administrators. These three could talk openly and frankly with the country's leadership. They had good personal contacts with the president, and could converse with him in a spirit of mutual respect and understanding.

At the time I expected the Pakistan program to blow up in our face. Luckily it didn't, but a well-fed supervisor on the other side of the world jeopardized the food supply of a nation with 50 million hungry inhabitants by removing *the whole management team to conform to a foolish administrative fiat.*

In retrospect, by keeping that team on a few more years, then moving it to other hungry countries, the Ford Foundation could have brought about a series of magnificent makeovers. Its staff had unparalleled experience. Sadly, a team with such complementary talents and panoramic competence to fight hunger would never again be assembled.

According to estimates, the seed imported from Mexico saved from three to five years in developing the better harvests. About three quarters of the 6 million or so acres of the dwarf wheat planted in Pakistan in the fall of 1968 came from Staley Pitts' humanitarian heist two years before. Together, then, those shipments had saved millions of lives. Though most of the seed was initially grown in irrigated areas, the contribution was vital, especially during the famine years.

Looking back we can see that the 1968 wheat harvests in both India and Pakistan were hardly one-time phenomena or flukes of nature. They provided 65 percent of South Asia's dietary calories and they have continued rising for five decades and more.

The revolution in wheat production boosted farm and national income. Studies showed that Indian and Pakistani farmers had lifted their income from $15 to $66 per acre. The extra production above the record 1964 base during the following four harvests added $3 billion to India's gross agricultural production and more than $1 billion to Pakistan's.

This extra buying power stimulated rural industry by increasing demand for fertilizers, pumps, machinery and other materials and services. It also increased personal spending. People invested mostly in home improvement. They built new houses, added new rooms, made major repairs, and installed electricity, running water, and improved latrines.

Among the greatest life changes was a huge reduction in drudgery. After the first big wheat crop in 1968, there were no more unsold tractors accumulating outside the factories. By 1969 five factories were annually churning out 18,000 tractors a year, India was importing 35,000 more, and the demand had soared so much that prospective purchasers had to make written application and wait a year or two for delivery.

Above all, mechanized cereal production provided better jobs and higher wages. It increased the efficiency of human effort. In those areas that adopted the new varieties most extensively, the demand for labor actually increased. In the peak periods there was a huge shortage of workers, where in the past there'd been a shortage of jobs.

Mechanization also brought more subtle effects. Employing threshers to separate the grain from the straw, for example, released the bullocks for preparing the land for the summer crop, rice. Timely land preparation was also behind the demand for tractors. It was a record bumper harvest that dumped an unexpected additional 5 million tons of wheat into the market.

There was some unrest. The landless wanted in on the farmers' "wealth." In December, 1968, in Tanjore, one of India's model agricultural-development districts, 42 persons were burned to death in a tragic clash between two groups of landless laborers. They were fighting over how best to get a share of the benefits from the new seeds

TOUR OF . . .

To tour the Punjab in 1968 was to see Mexican wheat stretching to the far horizon. Every corner of the land seemed to ne packed with the dense heads of Mexican dwarfs. A new spirit hung over the land. The sky seemed to have lifted. Farmers in turbans were excited. Indian scientists were excited . . . .

. . . TRIUMPH

.... And Borlaug and Glenn Anderson, his Canadian comrade in arms, were excited too. All of them had brought this transformation about. It was a food-production revolution that transcended language, nationality, personality and place in society. It was just humanity.

seeds being planted by landowners in the district. One group was willing to work at prevailing wage rates; the other wanted to enforce a boycott against the farms where the new seeds were being planted until landlords agreed to raise wages and share some of the handsome profits that were being realized with those who owned no land. [*New York Times*, December 28, 1968, p.3.]

1969
Perfection

A S THE TUMULTUOUS DECADE enters its last year of life Borlaug's dwarf wheats are conquering the world by stealth and surprise. Across South Asia that January, farmers have sown them on more than half Pakistan's 15-million-acre wheatland and more than a third of India's 35-million-acre wheatland. Just six years after a few grams of seed first arrived on this side of the world, Borlaug wheats occupy 15 times more area than in Mexico.

The origins of this amazing transformation hearken back to 1955 when he'd discovered eight seeds in a frayed and forgotten envelope. Those had been sown in pots deep inside a building and surrounded my muslin shrouds to protect the plants from stem rust. Since those vulnerable half-height plants were cross-pollinated in February 1956 he's completed 8156 more cross-pollinations in the attempt to make them practical as crops. Now their descendants have spread to so many countries that the entire wheat crop of the world has begun shrinking and global food production has begun soaring. A year back Turkey bought 20,000 tons of seed and now has almost 2 million acres in production. Afghanistan has 300,000 acres. Both are nearly producing all the bread they can eat. Others are starting down that same road.

This has been called a rare example of a discovery delivering more than promised. And it has been accomplished while Borlaug spent most of his time 12,000 miles away engaged in formal duties in remote parts of Mexico. He's never lived in Asia. He's been there basically one month a year for seven years. On the back of those quick trips – squeezed in during the month of March while he guiltily skipped his real duties – has come the present triumph. Seven months in seven years, plus a few snap visits to put out bush fires, is all it took. And he was the first to note that it was the plants and the other people who did the heavy lifting.

During his seventh March Mission in 1969 Norm, together with Narvaez and two local agriculturists began by visiting each of Pakistan's wheat-producing areas. The crop was advancing toward maturity, and wherever Mexipaks had been employed the fields shone with a goldening glow. In several places the seed was being multiplied on a massive scale. In others, both the white and red versions were in extensive production. The new era of pint-sized plants had finally arrived.

Most impressive of all, however, was the national mood swing. Famine is forgotten. Effervescent enthusiasm prevails. Farmers are ecstatic over their good fortune. Extension workers eagerly promote the new tools of their agronomy trade. Research scientists are working on grand future possibilities. Even normally reluctant government officials are eager to lend their support. Optimism had penetrated even the national psyche.

Norm saw it all:

> During the second half of February and the early days of March 1969 the crop was approaching maturity, and I accompanied Nacho, Qureshi and Z.A. Munshi to observe the outcome in each of the important production areas. What we found was astonishing. Wherever the Mexican seed was employed the fields looked beautiful. The new varieties had made a difference but so had Ayub Khan's 1966 decision to pay the international market price. The farmers had responded not only by planting more wheat but by managing their fields better. They were now striving to tease the utmost from their land. It was clear that within a month the harvest would be huge.

As a sort of finale to the decade and its own involvement the Ford Foundation brought together in Pakistan most of the Wheat Apostles Borlaug had trained in Mexico. There were by then more than 50. It was a celebratory occasion none would ever forget. For one thing, they felt a bond – a companionship of service in the fields of humankind. For another, they could see on all sides the worth of their efforts. Norm explains:

> Those trainees were really the ones that brought about the changes in the food supplies in hungry nations. They were from many countries, other than India. New Delhi had at last relented

and sent some students for training in Mexico, but it barred them from joining this reunion next door. I was sad that politics had interceded; everything we'd done prior to that had transcended politics, culture, language, and scientific background.

Stakman was there and the vice-president of the Ford Foundation, F.F. Hill was there. Frosty Hill was George Harrar's friend, which was why the two foundations had collaborated so well. He'd previously been a professor of economics and vice president of Cornell University, but he was a down-to-earth character who'd grown up on the land and was steeped in practical farming knowledge.

We took the whole group from the Northwest Frontier Province to Punjab and on south all the way to Sindh. It was the runup to the harvest. Everywhere, we saw beautiful fields of wheat. Everywhere, we saw the farmers' enthusiasm. Everywhere we examined the fields, visited farms and talked with public officials.

My constant concern was that a disease might unexpectedly show up. By now the Mexican dwarfs had spread to more than half the country's wheat acreage. That put a big responsibility on my shoulders. But everywhere the plants were healthy.

It was on this trip that Frosty Hill gave me a prediction: "Norm," he said, "enjoy this while you can. You'll never see it again. From now on things will just get worse. Bureaucrats will kill your whole darn program."

I didn't believe a word of it. After all, we had these wonderful plants. We had this wonderful cadre of Wheat Apostles. We had the ongoing training program and research operations in Mexico, Pakistan, India and six other nations. What could possibly go wrong?

After returning to Islamabad, Borlaug, Narvaez and Oddvar Aresvik called on the president:

> We went to inform Ayub Khan of the success that was shaping up. We told him that the early hopes of the wheat production campaign had become a reality. Pakistan's farmers were close to producing — or were even then producing — all the wheat Pakistan needed. Moreover, the country had the capacity to sustain a full food supply for the next 20 years if the research programs and the stimulatory economic policies were continued.
>
> We mentioned that there were 28 thoroughly trained Pakistani wheat scientists, who could maintain the program if provided proper political backing and financial support.
>
> Narvaez and Aresvik then informed President Ayub that the Ford Foundation considered their mission completed; within a few days they'd be transferred to Lebanon.
>
> President Ayub thanked us as well as the Ford and Rockefeller

WHEAT . . .

In 1969 all the young men who'd trained in Mexico since the program began in 1961 were brought together in Pakistan. During their six months in Sonora and Central Mexico they had participated in the effort to perfect the dwarf wheats. Now they could see the results of their collective efforts.

. . . . APOSTLES

By then they had helped transfer dwarf wheats to their own nations, and were playing a large part in spreading the high-yield wheats that lifted the horror of hunger from much of the world. An observer noted: "We could feel the spirit among them, it was energizing, satisfying; almost tangible."

Foundations. As we were about to leave his office, he pinned to my jacket the Sitara-I-Imtiaz, a medal shaped like a half circle with moon and stars.

Especially fitting was the manner in which the president said goodbye to Narvaez. At the close of our visit he walked to the car not with me, but with Nacho. As he pumped Nacho's hand for the last time he said: "Thank you, sir, for what you have done for Pakistan."Then the president mentioned in confidence that he'd had three heart attacks. Not even the Pakistani people knew. And the next day he'd be stepping down. The morning newspapers would explain that he was calling for new elections and turning responsibilities of government over to a caretaker president.

Next day, Ayub Khan did just that. His army chief of staff, Mohammad Yahya Khan, became the acting president. Considered the "Patton of Pakistan," this former general would make a good interim leader.

Or so it was thought.

That day the power changed hands happened to be Norm's 55th birthday – 25 March 1969 – and he spent it ensconced in the Ford Foundation staff house struggling to compose a readable account of all the wonders he'd seen.

That afternoon his train of thought was rudely interrupted by the shrill telephone; four economists wanted to come by the next day, would he see them? Borlaug agreed, but only reluctantly and only after they'd declared it urgent and *very* important.

When the economists arrived, three proved to be from a Harvard Group working under a World Bank grant; the other was with Pakistan's Agency of Procurement.

To Norm's amazement, they were perturbed about the size of the harvest that was shaping up. It was going to be so huge, they avowed, that the government could not keep its promise. There weren't enough rupees. The harvest would bankrupt Pakistan.

The four financial-fortune-tellers had computed that the payment could not exceed 18 rupees per maund, and were going to recommend that amount. They asked Borlaug to back them in this decision.

Norm instantly refused:

"The government announced that price before the crop was planted," I told them. "You cannot renege on it now. The farmers made their plans and committed themselves to loans and obligations based on that pledge. If you reduce the price now, with elections for a new president coming up, you're going to create political chaos. I won't back you at all."

Four disgruntled economists left the staff house muttering about dumb scientists. But for Norm fairness for farmers was paramount. Ten million peasants who'd soon be laboring to bring in the harvest had kept faith with their country. They'd made good their promise to Ayub to produce a record harvest of over 8 million tons. By their efforts they'd kept every Pakistani fed. They should not be cheated.

Nacho Narvaez was by now revered. In less than three years he'd moved not only programs but people – even the nation. His final days were replete with testimonial dinners, state tributes, and parties arranged by friends, colleagues and team members.

The journalist Wayne Swegle documented the scene as colleagues showed their respect: "I listened in on some of the final visits he had with administrators, wheat botanists, and research workers. They discussed the future of wheat improvement programs which would be carried out after Narvaez left West Pakistan. But the talk kept slipping back to incidents of the past. They recalled with great feeling their days of trial, of triumph, of frustration, of building. I heard the voices of grown men — scientists — quaver with emotion as they recalled the past together and contemplated the future without their friend and advisor."

Anwar Hussain, the research director who'd once dismissed Mexican wheats in front of the press and agriculture secretary Khuda Bakhsh said of Narvaez: "He will leave his shadow behind. And his shadow will remain with us for a long, long time. We will rely on his shadow."

Across the nearby border the new harvest marked a turning point. India was a step behind, but was operating on a much larger scale. There too problems of the past seemed over, and effervescent enthusiasm prevails.

Norm was amazed:

India's rural regions, which before had been so apathetic, were embracing to the new reality. Indeed, a kind of "wheat fever" was infecting everyone, including farmers both large and small, scientists, extension workers, professors, politicians and even the civil servants, whom everyone assumed to be immutable.

RURAL INDIA . . .

By 1969 Indian farming had a new look and a new level of production. Farmers like this one in the Punjab were getting up to 3 tons of wheat where before they'd harvested 700kg. In 1960 Punjab had produced 3.2 million tons of wheat and rice; in the decades ahead it will produce 26 million tons.

. . . AFTER BORLAUG

Borlaug seeds and the package of procedures that brought out their best turned Punjab into India's granary. Without these short, stiff-stalked highly productive Borlaug wheats India could not have sustained its population. Nor could it have risen in economic strength to its position among leading nations.

HONORING THE SAVIOR

March, 1969. Punjab Agricultural University, Ludhiana. Borlaug is awarded an honorary Doctor of Science, the first of many. This one was especially meaningful because it came from the university that had spearheaded the effort to introduce his seeds. At the time of this ceremony, Ludhiana, the city where the university is located was swamped with grain. Only two years before, India had faced its famine crisis.

Around this time Borlaug got to know B.P. Pal on a personal level. Pal was the research director who had been present at the pivotal IARI luncheon. He was a very cultured gent of around 60 who spoke impeccable English, learned while studying crop science at Cambridge University. Among other talents he could recount limericks, some quite spicy, for hours at a stretch. And he was both a philosopher and a world-renowned breeder of ornamental plants.

No wonder Norm enjoyed the company of this mild spoken perfect gentleman whom Alphabet Rao had once accused of fudging test results so Mexican wheats could be released for general planting. When the name B.P. Pal came up, Norm always smiled as if recalling some pleasant incident, which he was:

THE TORCH GETS PASSED

June 8, 1969. "MEXICAN NATIONAL IS HONORED BY PURDUE," read the
headlines. President Frederick L. Hovde confers an honorary degree of Doctor of
Agriculture by Purdue University on "one of Purdue's most distinguished alumni,
Ignacio Narvaez of Mexico." This is the very same F.L. Hovde who in 1933 gave an
Iowa farm boy a second chance at an education after he'd flunked the University of
Minnesota entrance exam. That farm-boy failure was named Norman Borlaug. Now
36 years later his right hand man is being honored for helping feed the world. The
benefactor of 1933 is now President of Purdue.

One afternoon B.P. Pal escorted me around the flower garden at
his home in Delhi, which he shared with his spinster sister. He
showed me gorgeous roses and bougainvilleas he'd bred.

After an hour or so he said, "Let's go up on the verandah and
have some tea." We got there, and over tea and biscuits he
leaned across the little table, looked me in the eye, and said:
"How are we doing?" I thought he was referring to India's overall
food supply; but then he added: "Are we still chasing too many
academic butterflies?"

That was a shock to my conscience. I immediately worried that
my harsh language must have offended him. Then I noticed a
mischievous gleam in his eye.

Only then did it hit me that Ralph Cummings had never edited
my original report, as I'd asked; he'd sent it on to the Indians
with all the typos and misspellings as well as all my hot and hasty
comments.

About the first of August, the most shocking telegram of all landed in Mexico. At the time, Norm was involved with the standard second-stanza work at Toluca on the mountain plateau near the capital:

> When I was working out of Mexico City in the summer of '69, I got probably the harshest communication I ever received. It was from Pakistan's new leader, and said in essence: "get your ass over here and explain this mess you've put me in."
>
> The language wasn't perhaps that crude but that's how I remember it. No national leader ever addressed me in terms so coarse, and I had no clue as to what I'd done wrong.
>
> Though Ayub was a gentleman – polished, smart, and a farmer to his soul – his successor was volatile and vulgar, given to cursing and indulgence. He was by far the crudest world leader I've met.
>
> At the time I knew nothing about Yahya Khan, and returned to Pakistan in all innocence and great puzzlement. In our first few minutes together he chewed me out with a level of abusiveness I'd never before experienced. In the same presidential palace where I'd been awarded the silver medal of distinction about four months earlier I now received a tongue lashing.
>
> "You wrote that damned report," Yahya screamed, "and you've destroyed me! In April we used your prediction to announce the country had achieved self-sufficiency in wheat. But you were way off the mark. There's not nearly enough to feed the country. I'm being forced to import 2 million tons more and that will ruin the country."
>
> "Look," I said, "There's something wrong here. I just can't believe that I overestimated the harvest by 2 million tons; I can't be that far off."
>
> "Well," he said, "You better damn well find out what's wrong, and fast!"
>
> "Give me a week. Don't do anything before that."

This request was granted. Norm had seven days to rescue his reputation and regain for the program the government's support. To make matters much worse he was coming down with pneumonia and felt terrible:

> Knowing there was no way I could complete the investigation in so short a time while alone and sick, I wired Narvaez in Lebanon and wrote Anderson in India and said "come on over right away; we've got big problems."
>
> Then I got a Ford Foundation car and driver and visited a few big farmers whom we'd worked with in the Punjabi farming area

THE DUPE

Yahya Khan, President of Pakistan. Successor to the cool and farsighted Ayub Khan who'd supported the wheat work, Yahya found himself out of his depth with agricultural policy. In his relations with Borlaug he proved coarse and demanding, but nonetheless took Borlaug's advice and saved his nation grief.

around Lahore. These were relatively prosperous farmers with a few hundred acres and warehouses in which to store their harvest.

"How much did your wheat yield?" I asked the first one.

"Oh, the harvest was good."

"Well, how much was the yield?"

"I don't have the tonnage because I haven't sold any grain yet. It's all piled up in the godown over there." "Why is that?"

"The government cut the price just when the harvest was beginning."

Then I went to another big farmer, and a third. Same story.

Every farmer with storage was holding his harvest. Though partly a protest, this was mainly done to force the prices up.

By then my pneumonia was roaring, and I had to take to my bed at the Ford Foundation guesthouse. When Nacho and Glenn arrived they came to my room and I croaked out what had happened. "The farmers are withholding their grain from the market," I said. "But before we tell the president we've got to get proper data. Our explanation must be fully confirmed and absolutely beyond question."

After that, the two of them scattered across the countryside; visiting government warehouses and interviewing farmers. Within five days they had the situation well documented. Small farmers had sold at the lower price to pay back the moneylenders, but the big farmers were holding the country's food supply to ransom.

Moreover, the situation was getting more tense and more difficult by the day. Wheat stocks in the government warehouses were falling at twice the monthly rate of wheat consumption. That meant half of what was being bought was merely being hoarded.

All that rampant speculation had sent wheat and bread prices soaring. The masses were getting restive; the government was too, but it couldn't do much. Speculators had it over a barrel.

I was out of things by then; Glenn wrote most of brief report. The summary declared:

- Large quantities of grain are still in the warehouses of large farmers;
- The original estimate of production was close to correct; and
- The government's reneging on the pre-sowing procurement price was largely responsible for large producers withholding their grain from the market, thereby resulting in playing into the hands of grain traders and speculators to the detriment of consumers and the embarrassment of the government.

Finally, we went to the president's office to hand over the report and present our conclusions in person. It was not an easy meeting:

Yahya Khan was still boiling mad. He seemed on the sharp edge of a violent outburst, and our message didn't calm him one bit.

Glenn spoke first. He told the president: "We think that Borlaug was probably close to correct; Pakistan has produced enough wheat to be self-sufficient or close to it. There is no 2-million ton deficit."

Then I gave a brief summary and handed over the report. "Cutting the price of wheat," I said, "destroyed the farmers' confidence in your government and provoked the current crisis."

Then, remembering the hurtful, expletive-filled cablegram, I decided to speak up more boldly: "Mr. President, you were responsible. Your price cut was why the wheat didn't move into the market. The big farmers knew they had the government under the gun. If you put the price back up, all the missing grain will reappear."

I was now watching him closely, and saw his expression change by visible degrees. My words weren't going down well. Yahya then began swearing and slapping the report down on the edge of his desk. He did it over and over. Crash! Bang!

Glenn and Nacho were visibly shaken and probably feared I'd provoked a violent end for all of us. I certainly felt that was possible.

But then he looked straight at me and said something quite unexpected. "Five days after I took office a delegation of economists told me we'd grown so much wheat that the government couldn't buy it all at the official price. I asked them 'What should be done?" They replied, "Reduce the price to 18 rupees a maund."

When I heard those words, things suddenly made sense. I knew immediately it had to be the same group who in March had wanted me to share responsibility for slashing the promised price.

"I took their advice," Yahya continued, "and now you tell me this is what caused the shortages and the black-market prices."

He looked at me intently as if willing me to devise an answer. "Yes," I replied, "and the sooner you restore the procurement price to 21 rupees, the sooner the grain will flow into the market. That will reduce the hoarding as well as the black market. It will bring down the price of bread."

Yahya remained violently angry and clearly distraught, but I paid no heed. "If there isn't enough money to pay for it," I said, "you should print more because the country's political stability is at stake. There's now a lack of confidence in the government that wasn't there before. Better to print more money than to have a political explosion. The countryside is quiet and peaceful even though three political parties are campaigning for the election. If you mix in food-price rises and bread shortages, political chaos will again erupt across Pakistan."

This was bitter medicine for the caretaker president, who was in a politically weak situation. However, he quickly restored the originally promised floor price, and the whole harvest came flooding onto the market. Then the price of bread returned to normal. The crisis passed.

Three months later, when all the political and economic dust had settled, the harvest was officially estimated to have been 6.618 million tons. Borlaug had been right on target. Pakistan was out of danger from famine. It no longer needed other countries' wheat. There'd be bread for all. The price would be right. And many benefits would go to Pakistani subsistence farmers.

Norm's efforts had thus reached fruition.

> I heard all kinds of yield estimates—mostly ranging from 7 million to 8 million tons. The government routinely estimates about 20 percent below actual production and several authorities think actual production was nearer nine million tons. Out of the crop harvested in the spring of 1969 about a million tons proved surplus to local needs. Overnight Pakistan became a wheat exporter. By May 1969, it was shipping about 100,000 tons to East Pakistan per month.

This was an amazing turn of events. This country had gone from beggar to bountiful in merely a couple of years.

In late 1969, William Gaud, Administrator of the U.S. Agency for International Development wrote in USAID's annual report that something important was happening to spectacularly increase yield in wheat and rice production in Pakistan and India. As a former supply officer during World War II he'd helped get food and equipment into China he knew what that signified. He called it a "Green Revolution."

To the world at large the title seemed apt, but, despite using the words probably more than any other individual, Norm never cottoned to the name. This omnibus term included rice, and as its highest-profile personality he'd be often saddled with criticisms that were irrelevant to wheat and his work. One of these was pesticides, something he'd almost never had to use. Indeed, he'd spent the bulk of his career working to immunize the wheat plant from stem rust and other fungi and thereby ensured it would not need fungicide sprays.

Nevertheless, AID director Gaud did history a service by lumping the two crops into the vast uplift in food that dubbed the Green Revolution. Since its founding in 1960 the International Rice Research Institute in the Philippines had done a spectacular job. By 1965 its brilliant rice breeder Hank Beachell had created IR8, a sturdy dwarf that carried genes for fast maturity, disease resistance, high yield, stiff stalk. Beachell's rice was the counterpart of Borlaug's dwarf wheat. By 1969 its contribution was being felt throughout Asia. India alone was using it on more than 6 million acres and Pakistan was on the way to becoming a substantial exporter of rice.

These two cereal grains, Mexican dwarf wheat and Philippine dwarf rice touched off the transformation that changed the global dynamic. They are what stopped hunger from going global and going guerilla. By now there is enough food to accommodate the current 3 billion humans. And people know what to do to stave off catastrophe as 3 billion more try to join the human race.

This is where the trial of a whole generation came before the great judge. And all of a sudden humanity is less unhappy.

The possibilities these two opened seemed almost endless. In 1969, for instance, it became clear that dwarf wheat and dwarf rice could be grown like a relay race each year *in the same ground*. Their fast-maturity and ability to grow out of season, made possible this double cropping. With them, good farmers could grow 2 tons of wheat during the winter season and 3 tons of rice during the summer season on each acre of land.

Accomplishing that feat required precision and competence. But in both India and Pakistan it ushered in another big wave of food production. Farmers who'd previously expected to harvest 3 tons of wheat during the winter season could now add that much or more with a crop of rice during the summer. It took heavy fertilization and proper field management, but millions saw their income soar and their families say goodbye to poverty.

The fact that every year 5 or more tons of food could be harvested from the same acre that had previously yielded little more than half a ton brought a wholesale change in perspective. For the first time yields were calculated on the basis of production **per year**.

A few of the most progressive farmers used triple cropping, involving wheat followed by mung bean followed by rice. Some grew wheat then rice then potato – all within 12 months. By increasing the intensity of cropping, both food production potential and employment increased without expanding the farmland area.

By this time it was clear that the Mexican seed imports – so courageously ordered against intense opposition and never-ending difficulties – saved from three to five years in reaping the benefits from the better harvests. In Pakistan, for example, about three quarters of the 6 million or so acres of the dwarf wheat grown in 1969 came from Staley Pitts' 50 tons of seed, imported under less-than-legal auspices in 1966. A lot of lives were on the line during those years. Without the extra food those 4.5 million acres provided the country would not have been at all well off.

Much of the early income was spent on a new and potent insurance against drought and famine. You see, water had been discovered beneath the feet of millions of Indians and Pakistani farmers. That groundwater, which was recharged annually with outflow from the Himalayas, could be tapped by a pipe driven into the gound sometimes no more than 10 feet. At the decade's beginning India had had 160,000 of these "tubewells"; now the number was climbing toward 8,000,000.

This was important because the main problem of producing more food was no longer the seed and no longer the soil . . .it was the water supply. Most of the year most of Pakistan and northern India is achingly dry.

How the impoverished villagers found the money to pay for 70,000 tubewells was a mystery. The Pakistani tubewell specialist, Ghulam Mohammed set out to determine how so many impoverished families found the necessary $1500, which was more money than they made in a year.

Norm knew Ghulam Mohammed well. He was an authority on water and salinity and was responsible for fostering the use of tube wells in Pakistan. He spent one summer in Mexico investigating irrigation and soil drainage, and Norm had taken him to Sonora, where he was amazed at the progress.

Unfortunately, he suffered from tuberculosis, but before he died he solved the mystery: The tubewells were bought with the gold bangles from farm wives' arms. Those bracelets were not so much for beauty as for banking, and when the proper investment opportunity arrived the women cashed in their bangles. He also found that within three years they had twice as many gold bangles on their arms, thanks to a tubewell and Mexican wheat.

There were huge increases in nitrogen fertilizer consumption in India (from 58,000 tons in 1950 to 538,000 in 1964 and 1.2 million tons of nutrients in 1969). And about 60 percent of this amount was produced domestically. A large part of the fertilizer was used for wheat.

There was even a political change. Before this time it had been mooted that private industry, relying on the profit motive, would be an impediment to economic development; government, it was said, must supply the needed goods and services. But the Green Revolution advanced at a rate more rapid than government could service. The pressure for fertilizer and insecticide became great enough to weaken and overcome the ideological commitment to government-run industry.

Mechanization was a part of the wheat revolution that fascinated Norm.

The critics had universally proclaimed that the mechanization of agriculture would be bad for Indian conditions, where so much labor was available. "You don't really need mechanization," they'd always said. "You'll be putting people out of work."

But with the introduction of the short-duration, high-yielding dwarf wheats, mechanization became a feasible proposition. In fact it became vital. When the time between two crops was short, the value of precision and timeliness in operations became clear to everyone . . . that is what stabilized the system at high yield levels.

Mechanization brought seed drills, pumping sets for irrigation, harvesters and threshers; there were also storage bins, and so on. This made life livable for millions.

The increased mechanization tended to increase the employment but more importantly provided better jobs and higher wages. Moreover, it helped reduce drudgery and increased the efficiency of human energy. In those areas that adopted the new varieties most extensively, there was actually a shortage of workers at the peak seasons.

Mechanization also brought subtle, indirect but nonetheless very important changes. For example, when small mechanical threshers were used to separate the grain from the straw, the bullocks were released for use in preparing the land for the next crop. This need for timely preparation of land was also one of the main reasons for the surge in demand for tractors.

When you traveled in the countryside in 1969, South Asia looked very different. Farm families were investing in better storage facilities. Brick houses were replacing the mud-walled huts. Electricity was lighting the nights and driving the motors. Sewing machines were popular. Transistor radios brought entertainment, education, new visions and useful advice into remote villages. And demand for consumer goods was soaring.

Home improvement ranked high. For some that meant building a new houses, for others an extension to an old one or major repairs. To many it meant the installation of electricity, running water, or sanitation. A sitting room was a common addition. A room kept apart from daily use was a status symbol – it was, one report says, "a newly-gained place to show one's self, one's family and to denote one's achievements to visitors, and of course to gossip with the neighbors – a mark that the family, if not fully arrived, is at least on the way."

Clothing ranked right after buildings, not just because it was an essential but because, again, it was one way of boosting self respect, as well as a way to add brightness to life.

Transportation was a popular purchase. Bicycles, motor scooters and motorcycles were to be seen in the remote villages. Truck and bus service was improving.

Now when rural regions demanded better roads, better public transportation and better schools, they got them. Soon bicycles, motor scooters and motorcycles could be seen in the most distant villages, and truck and bus service became routine so villagers could for the first time enjoy the freedom of travel.

Within the rural areas all this generated a climate of confidence. Optimism was on the rise. The seeds had helped South Asia; and now South Asia was helping itself.

Moreover, the bountiful production of grain forced the governments to provide public services. Starting in 1969, stimulated in part by criticism from farmers and the press, warehouse capacity was greatly expanded to provide storage for the rising quantities of grain. Villagers demanded better roads, better public transportation and better schools; and began getting them.

Sadly, this transformation failed to seize a place in the general histories of the decade or the century. It's never been properly understood or appreciated. However, certain writers have provided a